广东风味菜

GUANGDONG FLAVOROUS DISHES

汤　　羹

TASTY SOUP

李曾鹏展　著

广东科技出版社

目錄

自序

　　陸羽寫「茶經」，隨園編食譜，意在啓發後人學習烹飪。蔬菜雖微，巧爲炮製，亦能引起食欲，有助家庭歡樂，促進社交友誼。現代學校，列烹飪爲女生家政之一者，非無因也。

　　家慈精炊事，鵬展耳聞目覩，幼受薰陶，長從名廚學習，因而稍識門徑，得友好鼓勵，先在麗的電視示範，又在香港電台主持「食在香港」節目，復蒙先進不棄，邀列講席，近年在無線電視之「婦女新姿」節目示範。隨教隨寫，彙成講義，非云獨具心得，聊供愛好者切磋，但願前輩有以敎之。

李曾鵬展

寫在湯羹之前

「三日入廚下，洗手作羹湯」，從唐朝詩人王建的「新嫁娘」中，可見古時候人們已經極爲注重湯羹。

廣東人向來最重湯水，湯水不僅是美食之一，如果用料適當，還可以調理身體。

烹煮湯羹，大致都是將材料和多量的水，共煮一段時間，煮好後材料的精華溶合在一起，湯水味道好，營養又豐富，湯渣可作菜餚，既省工夫，又不浪費材料，眞是一舉兩得。

湯羹的烹飪方法可細分成下面四種：燴、滾、煲、燉。

燴就是把多種材料切粒或切絲，經過處理後，用上湯煮滾，再加入粟粉或馬蹄粉水煮成稀糊，稱爲羹。

滾就是把材料切成小件，在煲或鑊把水燒滾，將處理好的材料放入滾熟便是。

煲就是把材料原塊或切件，經過處理後，放入已煲滾的水中，煲滾後改用慢火把材料熬出味，大約需要二至三小時，要視材料品質而定。

燉就是將材料原塊或切件，經過處理，放入燉盅內，加入滾水後蓋上盅蓋，再用沙紙封密盅口，放入已有水的鑊或煲內，蓋上鑊或煲蓋，加熱，利用水蒸氣燉至材料出味。通常燉的時間都較煲爲長。

烹飪器皿推陳出新，除了傳統的以外，還有高速煲、電子瓦罉，這些新產品用來煲湯更爲方便。

用高速煲煲湯，把煲湯的時間縮短，當高速煲發出響聲後，將大火減慢，開始計時間，按照本菜譜指示的時間的三分之一便夠了。電子瓦罉則以水滾開始計時間，開強火掣，按本菜譜指示時間再加一倍，煲湯的水分則要照本菜譜提供的酌量減少。

本菜譜提供的照片，主要是讓讀者清楚地看到各種材料，並以視覺上的欣賞爲主，所以沒有把材料煲足夠時間，因爲煲得太久，有些材料不容易辨認出來。

「蒸」和「煲仔菜」出版後，得到讀者和觀眾的支持鼓勵，在此致最深的謝意。當「湯羹」和各位見面時，請繼續給我支持和提出意見，待我有所改進。

李曾鵬展

本菜譜常用之廚具

雞、鴨

荔荷燉雞

用料：

瘦光雞一隻，約重二斤，江瑤柱半兩，桂味荔枝二十個（去皮去核），荷花一朵或新鮮荷葉八分一件。

做法：

(1)瑤柱洗淨用清水浸二小時，撕幼。

(2)荷花取花瓣洗淨，如用荷葉也要洗淨。

(3)雞放落滾水煮十分鐘，取起洗淨。怕湯肥，撕去皮和膏。

(4)將瑤柱、雞、荷葉放落燉盅內，加入滾水六杯或適量（如用荷花要後下），放入煲內，燉三小時，下荔枝、荷花、鹽調味，冚密燉盅蓋，再燉半小時即成。取起荷葉不要，荷花可用以裝飾。

註：

(1)燉湯最好用沙紙封貼燉盅口，使香氣不外洩。

(2)燉盅放在鑊或煲內燉好後，很難取出，應該用一竹筲箕縛緊繩子作手挽，將燉盅放在筲箕內，然後放入材料，冚密蓋，

用沙紙封口，筲箕連燉盅放入煲或鑊內燉。當水滾而震動時，只是筲箕與煲相碰，不至影響燉盅。燉好後，用筷子挑出繩子作手挽，很易取出。

(3)燉湯的湯清，湯料較煲湯的嫩滑。

(4)如嫌燉湯麻煩，可改為煲湯，煲時水分酌量增加，時間略為減少。

CHICKEN WITH LYCHEE AND LOTUS LEAF SOUP

Ingredients:
1 chicken (about 2⅔ lb)
½ oz conpoy
20 lychees (skin and stone removed)
1 lotus flower or ⅛ lotus leaf

Method:
1. Wash conpoy and soak in water for 2 hours. Tear into thin stripes.
2. Wash petals of lotus flower (if lotus leaf is used, wash it as well).
3. Put chicken into boiling water to cook for 10 minutes. Take out and wash. To prevent the soup from getting too oily, remove the skin and fat of chicken.
4. Put conpoy, chicken and lotus leaf into steaming pot. Add 6 cups of boiling water and stew for 3 hours. (if lotus flower is used, it should be added later) Then put in lychees, lotus and salt. Stew for another ½ hour. Dispose lotus leaf and use the lotus flower for garnishment.

花旗參鮑魚雞湯

用料：

花旗參二錢半切片（花旗參不能太多，會有甘苦味），急凍鮑魚二隻，瘦雞一隻，薑二片，葱二條，酒半湯匙。

做法：

(1) 鮑魚、雞洗淨，如怕湯肥，把雞的膏和皮撕去。

(2) 薑二片，葱二條加半鑊水煮滾，放下鮑魚、雞煮十分鐘，取起洗淨。

(3) 水十四杯或適量煲滾，放下花旗參、鮑魚、雞、薑一片、酒半湯匙煲滾，慢火煲三小時。湯料盛碟上，湯加鹽及生抽一湯匙調味，盛湯碗內，一齊上桌。

註：

(1) 煲的湯可以改為燉湯，燉的方法把鮑魚、雞出水過冷河後，放入燉盅內，加入花旗參、薑、酒、滾水，水的分量視需要湯的分量而定。冚密燉盅蓋，燉四至五小時，燉的時間較煲的時間加長三分一。

(2) 燉湯的湯清，湯渣較滑。

(3) 可以把鮑魚改為螺頭、乾的螺片或乾的鮑魚片，乾的螺片和鮑魚片要用清水浸軟才煲，容易出味。

ABALONE AND CHICKEN WITH AMERICAN GINSENG SOUP

Ingredients:

⅓ oz American Ginseng
2 frozen abalone
1 chicken
2 slices ginger
2 stalks spring onion
½ tbsp wine

Method:

1. Wash abalone and chicken. To prevent soup from getting too oily, remove skin and fat from chicken.
2. Put 2 slices of ginger and 2 stalks spring onion in ½ wok of water. Bring to boil. Add abalone and chicken. Cook for 10 minutes. Take out and wash.
3. Boil 14 cups of water, put in American Ginseng, abalone, chicken, ginger and ½ tbsp wine. Bring to boil. Stew for 3 hours. Serve ingredients in plate. Add salt and 1 tbsp light soy to soup, serve in bowl.

雞酒湯

用料：

雞半隻，重一斤四両，木耳半両，花生肉二両，紅棗十粒去核，薑數片。

調味：

米酒三分一杯或適量，水四杯半或適量(可用煲花生的水)，鹽半茶匙。

做法：

(1)木耳用清水浸二小時洗淨，切小件，放落滾水中煮五分鐘，取起洗淨滴乾水，此法可除去木耳的異味。

(2)花生肉放落清水中煲滾，慢火再煲二十分鐘，冷後去衣洗淨，用適量水把花生肉煲腍，約需四十分鐘。

(3)雞斬件，如怕湯肥，可撕去肥油及皮才斬件。

(4)用半湯匙油爆香薑及雞，加入調味、木耳、花生、紅棗煮滾，慢火煮至雞熟，約需二十五分鐘。

註：

(1)雞酒湯是廣東產婦及老人的補品，活血養顏。

(2)米酒即是白色的酒，如玉冰燒米酒、雙蒸米酒、三蒸米酒，米酒分量視各人喜愛按照本菜譜加減。

CHICKEN AND WINE SOUP

Ingredients:
½ chicken (about 1³/₅ lb)
½ oz dried fungus
3 oz peanuts
10 dried red dates (stones removed)
few slices ginger

Seasoning:
¹/₃ cup rice wine
4½ cup water
½ tsp salt.

Method:
1. Soak dried fungus for 2 hours. Wash and shred. Put into boiling water to cook for 5 minutes. Wash and drain.
2. Put peanut in water and bring to the boil. Cook for 20 minutes. When cool, remove the skin. Stew for another 40 minutes until peanuts are tender.
3. Chop up chicken. Remove the skin and fat from the chicken to avoid soup from being too oily.
4. Saute ginger and chicken with ½ tbsp oil. Add seasoning, dried fungus, peanuts and dried red dates. Cook for 25 minutes until chicken is completely cooked.

菜膽雞燉翅

用料：

急凍魚翅一斤，光瘦雞一隻，白菜十二兩，中國火腿半兩，上湯六杯（最好另用一隻雞煲成上湯，或用罐頭清雞湯三杯，水三杯。如不用上湯只用水燉，就會淡而無味）。

出水料：

薑二片，葱二條，酒二湯匙，水五杯，油一湯匙。

調味：

鹽一茶匙或適量，薑一大片，酒三湯匙。

做法：

(1)白菜摘去老莖，切去菜尖，改成四至五吋長之菜膽，洗淨，放落滾水中灼熟，用清水浸冷後，取起滴乾水。

(2)把出水料煮滾，放下魚翅煮十分鐘，撈起滴乾水，薑、葱不要，魚翅放入燉盅內。

(3)雞放落滾水中煮十分鐘，取起洗淨，放在燉盅內的魚翅上（怕湯肥撕去雞油及皮），加入調味及火腿。把上湯煲滾加入，冚密燉盅蓋，燉三小時，加入菜膽再燉二十至三十分鐘，原盅上桌。

SHARK'S FIN WITH CHICKEN AND CABBAGE SOUP

Ingredients:
frozen shark's fin (about 1⅓ lbs)
1 chicken
1 lb white cabbage
½ oz Chinese ham
6 cups superior stock (prepared with a chicken or 3 cups of canned chicken broth mix with 3 cups of water)

Ingredients for stewing shark's fin:

2 slices ginger
2 stalks spring onion
2 tbsp wine
5 cups water
1 tbsp oil

Seasoning:

1 tsp salt
1 slice ginger
3 tbsp wine

Method:

1. Remove the hard stem of white cabbage and remove the tips. Cut into 4″–5″ sections. Wash and blanch in boiling water. Soak in water and drain.
2. Boil the ingredients for stewing shark's fin. Put in shark's fin to cook for 10 minutes. Drain and dispose ginger, spring onion. Put shark shark's fin into steaming a pot.
3. Put chicken in boiling water to cook for 10 minutes. Take out and wash. Place on top of shark's fin. Add seasoning and ham. Boil stock and put in pot as well. Cover the pot with a lid. Stew for 2 hours. Add the cabbage and stew for another 20–30 minutes. Serve in pot.

海南椰子煲雞湯

用料：

瘦光雞一隻，洋葱一隻切絲，椰子肉一個。

做法：

(1)椰子肉批去黑皮洗淨。

(2)洋葱絲用半湯匙油爆香鏟起，用熱水洗一洗以去油。

(3)雞撕去肥膏，放落滾水中煮十分鐘，取起洗淨。

(4)水十杯或適量煲滾，放下雞、椰子肉、洋葱煲滾後，慢火煲三小時。湯料盛碟上，湯加鹽調味，一齊上桌。

註：

可以用牛尾代替雞，煲牛尾最好加入二條西芹，可除牛尾之羶味。

HOINAM STYLE COCONUT AND CHICKEN SOUP

Ingredients:
1 chicken
1 shredded onion
1 coconut meat

Method:
1. Remove the dark skin of coconut, wash.
2. Saute spring onion with ½ tbsp oil. Wash with hot water to remove the oil.
3. Remove the fat from the chicken. Put into boiling water to cook for 10 minutes. Take out and wash.
4. Boil 10 cups of water. Put in chicken, coconut and onion. Bring to boil, then stew for 3 hours. Serve the ingredients in plate. Add salt to soup and serve in bowl.

冬菇鳳爪湯

用料：

冬菇二両，鳳爪十二隻（雞腳斬去腳棍稱鳳爪），馬蹄肉六隻（切開邊），薑一片，葱二條，清雞湯二罐，水四杯。

醃料：

鹽四分三茶匙，糖三分一茶匙，酒二茶匙，生粉三分一茶匙，油一湯匙。

做法：

(1)鳳爪洗淨放落滾水中煮五分鐘，取起洗一洗。

(2)冬菇浸軟去腳揸乾水，加醃料撈勻（冬菇一定要浸透，薄的浸二小時，厚的要浸三小時，如果浸不透，食時有木味）。

(3)清雞湯及水煲滾後，下薑、葱、馬蹄、鳳爪煲滾，慢火煲四十分鐘，下冬菇再煲二十至二十五分鐘，取去薑、葱不要。

(4)如湯油多肥膩，用紙巾快速在湯面拖過，可去肥油。加鹽調味。

註：

(1)冬菇要買菇底白色的才香，如菇底咖啡色，即是放得太久了，吃時不香。

(2)冬菇不能煮得太久，煮得太久，靭而不香。

BLACK MUSHROOM WITH CHICKEN FEET SOUP

Ingredients:
2½ oz black mushroom
12 chicken feet
6 water chestnuts (halve)
1 slice ginger
2 stalks spring onion
2 cans chicken broth
4 cups water

Seasoning:
¾ tsp salt
$1/3$ tsp sugar

2 tsp wine
$\frac{1}{3}$ tsp cornflour
1 tbsp oil

Method:

1. Wash chicken feet and put into boiling water to cook for 5 minutes. Take out and wash.
2. Soak black mushrooms, squeeze out excess water and trim. Marinate with seasoning. (Mushroom must be thoroughly soaked, thin mushroom — 2 hours, thick ones — 3 hours)
3. Boil chicken broth and water, add ginger, spring onion, water chestnut and chicken feet. Stew for 40 minutes, put in mushrooms and cook for 20—25 minutes. Dispose ginger and spring onion.
4. If soup is getting too oily, use a tissue paper to draw away the floating fat. Season with salt.

北芪雞腳湯

用料：

雞腳六隻，乾豬腳筋一両，排骨六両斬件，紅棗六粒去核，北芪、黨參共一両，眉豆一両，薑一片。

做法：

(1)豬腳筋用清水浸透，約需八小時。

(2)雞腳剪去腳甲，洗淨。

(3)雞腳、豬腳筋、排骨放落滾水中煮五分鐘，取起洗淨。

(4)眉豆用清水浸半小時，隔去水分。

(5)水九杯或適量煲滾，放下雞腳、豬腳筋、排骨、眉豆、紅棗、北芪、黨參、薑煲滾後，慢火煲二小時半至三小時，加入鹽及生抽半湯匙調味，湯與湯料同上桌。

CHICKEN FEET WITH ASTRAGALUS HENGL SOUP

Ingredients:

6 chicken feet

1½ oz dried pig sinew

8 oz chopped spare ribs

6 dried red dates (stones removed)

1½ oz campanumaea pilosula and astragalus hengl

1½ of brow beans

1 slice ginger

Method:

1. Soak dried pig sinew for about 8 hours.
2. Remove the nails of chicken feet, wash.
3. Put chicken feet, pig sinew and spare ribs in boiling water to cook for 5 minutes. Take out and wash.
4. Soak brow beans ½ hour. Drain.

5. Boil 9 cups of water, put in chicken feet, pig sinew, spare ribs, beans, dried red dates, astragalus hengl,campanumaea pilosula and ginger. Cook for 2½–3 hours, add salt and ½ tbsp light soy, serve in bowl.

陳皮燉鴨湯

用料：

瘦光鴨一隻，重約一斤半至二斤，江瑤柱三粒，靚果皮一個，薑一片，八角半粒，酒一湯匙。

醃料：

薑汁半湯匙，酒半湯匙。

做法：

(1)江瑤柱用清水浸二小時。

(2)果皮浸軟洗淨，刮去囊。

(3)鴨撕去肥油，斬去腳，用牙簽刺破眼(以免炸時油彈起)，洗淨抹乾水，用醃料搽勻鴨肚內，用鐵針縫密肚口。再用老抽搽外皮，放落滾油中炸到金黃色撈起。

(4)鴨炸後，除去鐵針，放落滾水中煮十分鐘，以去肥油，取出洗一洗。

(5)鴨、果皮、瑤柱、薑、八角同放燉盅內，加滾水六杯或適量，冚密蓋燉三小時至四小時，落鹽調味。食時可把菜薳灼熟放入燉盅內，原盅上桌。

註：

(1)廣東有三寶：老薑、果皮、禾桿草。果皮又稱陳皮，以新會出產的最靚，陳皮燉鴨湯是粵菜傳統菜譜。

(2)陳皮有下氣之功效。

DUCK WITH DRIED TANGERINE PEEL SOUP

Ingredients:
1 duck (about 2 lb)
3 conpoy
1 dried tangerine peel
1 slice ginger
½ star anise
1½ tbsp wine

Seasoning:
½ tbsp ginger
½ tbsp wine

Method:
1. Soak conpoy for 2 hours.
2. Soak dried tangerine peel, wash.
3. Remove the fat from the duck, chop off the legs. Prick the eyes with toothpicks to avoid exploding while frying. Wash and wipe dry. Rub seasoning inside the duck. Stitch up with a pin. Then rub on dark soy outside of the duck. Deep fry until golden brown.
4. Remove the pin and put duck in boiling water to cook for 10 minutes. Take out to wash.
5. Put duck, tangerine peel, conpoy, ginger and star anise in a steaming pot. Add 6 cups of boiling water. Stew for 3—4 hours, add salt. When serve, blanch vegetable and put on top.

木瓜花生雞腳湯

用料：

半生熟木瓜十二両至一斤（在菜攤有賣），花生肉二両，雞腳八隻，排骨四両斬件，薑一片。

做法：

(1)木瓜去皮去核洗淨切件。

(2)花生肉用清水浸四十分鐘，隔去水分。要除去花生衣，把花生肉放落清水中煲二十分鐘，冷後去衣，洗淨。

(3)雞腳剪去腳甲洗淨。

(4)雞腳、排骨放落滾水中煮五分鐘，取起洗淨。

(5)水八杯或適量放入煲內，加入花生煲滾，加入木瓜、薑、排骨、雞腳，煲滾後，慢火煲一小時半，加鹽調味。

PEANUT, PAPAYA AND CHICKEN FEET SOUP

Ingredients:
1 lb papaya
3 oz peanuts
8 chicken feet
6 oz spare ribs (chopped)
1 slice ginger

Method:

1. Slice papaya, remove the core, wash and chop up.
2. Soak peanuts in water for 40 minutes. Drain. Then put in boiling water to cook for 20 minutes. When cool, remove the membrane and wash.
3. Cut the nails of chicken feet, wash.
4. Put chicken feet and spare ribs in boiling water to cook for 5 minutes. Take out and wash.
5. Boil 8 cups of water together with peanuts, bring to boil. Then add papaya, ginger, spare ribs and chicken feet. Bring to the boil and cook for 1½ hours. Season with salt.

耙齒蘿蔔煲鴨湯

用料：

耙齒蘿蔔一斤，光穀鴨一隻，重一斤至二斤，果皮四分一個（浸軟洗淨）。

做法：

(1)耙齒蘿蔔去皮洗淨，原隻或切厚件（原隻煲腍再切件）。

(2)鴨撕去肥油，切去尾部不要，因尾部両粒子有羶味。洗淨放落滾水中煮十分鐘，取起洗淨。

(3)水十杯或適量，放入果皮煲滾，加入鴨、蘿蔔煲滾後，慢火煲三小時。蘿蔔和鴨上碟，湯加適量的鹽及生抽半湯匙調味，盛湯碗內齊上桌。

註：

(1)煲湯的鴨小而瘦，骨硬，稱穀鴨，價錢平。穀鴨煲湯甜，可到街市雞鴨檔買，穀鴨已劏好，價錢以每隻計算。米鴨買時才劏，價錢按重量計算。米鴨肉厚膏多，不適宜煲湯，而且價錢貴。

(2)可以把鴨改為牛腩或排骨。

TURNIP WITH DUCK SOUP

Ingredients:

$1\frac{1}{3}$ lb turnip

1 duck (about $1\frac{1}{3}$ to $2\frac{2}{3}$ lb)

¼ dried tangerine peel (soaked and washed)

Method:

1. Skin and wash turnip, cut into

thick sections or whole turnip after being cooked.

2. Remove the fat from the duck and dispose the bottom. Wash and put in boiling water to cook for 10 minutes. Take out and wash.

3. Boil 10 cups of water together with tangerine peel. Add duck and turnip and stew for 3 hours. Serve turnip and duck in plate. Add salt and ½ tbsp light soy to soup, serve in bowl.

西洋菜
煲鮮陳腎湯

用料：

西洋菜半斤至十二両，臘鴨腎（又稱陳腎）二隻，新鮮鴨腎二隻，南杏半両，北杏數粒。

做法：

(1)臘鴨腎、新鮮鴨腎洗淨，放落滾水中煮五分鐘，取起洗淨。

(2)南北杏放落滾水中煮五分鐘，去衣。

(3)在清水中放下少許鹽，把西洋菜放在鹽水中浸半小時，洗淨滴乾水。西洋菜容易附有蜞乸（水蛭），用鹽水浸後，蜞乸會走出水面，容易除去。

(4)水八杯或適量煲滾，放下西洋菜、鮮陳腎、南北杏煲滾，慢火煲二小時，加入適量鹽調味，湯和西洋菜盛湯碗內。

(5)鮮陳腎切片上碟，蘸生抽熟油吃。

註：

煲時加入二粒瑤柱，湯更鮮美。

WATERCRESS WITH DRIED AND FRESH DUCK GIZZARD SOUP

Ingredients:
1 lb watercress
2 dried duck gizzard
2 fresh duck gizzard
½ oz almond
few bitter almond

Method:

1. Wash dried and fresh duck gizzards. Put into boiling water to cook for 5 minutes. Take out and wash.
2. Put the almonds in boiling water to cook for 5 minutes. Remove the membrane.
3. Soak watercress in salted water for ½ hour. Wash and drain.
4. Boil 8 cups of water. Put in watercress, gizzard and almonds. Bring to boil and simmer for 2 hours. Add salt and serve the soup as well as watercress in bowl.
5. Slice the gizzards and serve in plate.

金銀菜
臘鴨頭翼湯

用料：

菜乾半両，白菜半斤，臘鴨頭一
隻，臘鴨翼四隻，蜜棗三粒。

做法：

(1)菜乾用清水浸半小時，洗淨切
短度。

(2)白菜洗淨每棵切開邊。

(3)臘鴨頭切件，臘鴨翼每隻切開
兩件，放落滾水中煮五分鐘，
取起洗淨。

(4)水九杯或適量煲滾，將菜乾、
白菜、蜜棗、臘鴨頭、臘鴨翼
放落煲內煲滾，慢火煲二小
時，試味，如覺淡落鹽調味。

(5)湯盛湯碗內，湯料盛碟上，一
齊上桌。

註：

金銀菜即是菜乾和新鮮白菜。

FRESH AND DRIED CAB-BAGE WITH DRIED DUCK HEAD AND WING SOUP

Ingredients:
½ oz dried white cabbage
10 oz white cabbage
1 dried duck head
4 dried duck wings
3 dried red dates

Method:

1. Soak dried white cabbage for ½ hour. Wash and section.
2. Wash white cabbage and halve-vertically.
3. Slice duck head. Halve duck wings. Put into boiling water to cook for 5 minutes. Take out and wash.
4. Boil 9 cups of water. Add cabbage, dates, duck head and wings. Bring to boil and simmer for 2 hours. Add salt if necessary.
5. Serve soup in bowl and ingredients in plate.

芥菜滾燒鴨湯

用料：

芥菜半斤，燒鴨四分一隻（斬件），薑一片。

做法：

(1)燒鴨將肥膏撕去不要。

(2)芥菜洗淨切短度。

(3)水四杯或適量，薑一片放入煲內煲滾，下芥菜再煲滾後，慢火煲睒，約需十五分鐘，下燒鴨一滾即成，落鹽調味。

LEAF MUSTARD AND BARBECUE DUCK SOUP

Ingredients:

10 oz leaf mustard
¼ barbecue duck (chopped)
1 slice ginger

Method:

1. Remove the fat from barbecue duck.
2. Wash leaf mustard, section.
3. Boil 4 cups of water together with a slice of ginger. Add leaf mustard and bring to boil. Simmer for approximately 15 minutes until it's tender. Put in barbecue duck and bring to the boil. Season with salt.

豬、牛、羊

節瓜
章魚煲豬蹄湯

用料：

節瓜一斤，章魚乾二両(又稱八爪魚)，豬蹄肉十二両。

做法：

(1)節瓜刮去外皮洗淨，如節瓜大件，切爲二節。

(2)章魚用清水浸二十分鐘，洗淨。

(3)豬蹄放落滾水中煮五分鐘，取出洗淨。

(4)水十杯或適量，煲滾，放下節瓜、章魚、豬蹄煲滾，慢火煲二小時半。湯料切件上碟，湯加適量的鹽、生抽半湯匙調味，盛湯碗內齊上枱。

註：

可以用蓮藕代節瓜。

HAIRY GOURD, DRIED OCTOPUS AND PORK SOUP

Ingredients:
1$\frac{1}{3}$ lb hairy gourd
3 oz dried octopus
1 lb pork from knuckles

Method:
1. Skin and wash hairy gourd. Halve

if it's too big.

2. Soak dried octopus in water for 20 minutes. Clean.

3. Put pork in boiling water to cook for 5 minutes. Take out and wash.

4. Boil 10 cups of water, put in hairy gourd, dried octopus and pork. Bring to the boil and then simmer for 2½ hours. Chop the ingredients and dish up. Add salt and ½ tsp light soy to soup, serve in bowl.

P.S. Lotus roots can be used instead of hairy gourd.

粉葛
豬蹄煲蠔豉湯

用料：

粉葛一斤，豬蹄半斤，蠔豉十個，薑一片，葱二條。

做法：

(1)粉葛批去皮洗淨，切厚件。

(2)豬蹄放落滾水中煮五分鐘，取起洗淨。

(3)蠔豉用清水浸十五分鐘洗淨，加入滾水(要浸過蠔豉面)冚密，浸半小時，隔去水分。

(4)用半湯匙油，爆香薑、葱、蠔豉，加水約一杯煮片刻鏟起，棄去薑、葱，將蠔豉洗一洗，以去油膩。(此法能除去蠔豉之腥味)

(5)水十杯或適量煲滾，加入粉葛、豬蹄、蠔豉煲滾後，用慢火煲三小時半至四小時，落鹽調味。

(6)湯上窩，粉葛、豬蹄、蠔豉上碟，淋上少許生抽熟油同上桌。

註：

粉葛又名實心藕，用粉葛煲湯，最少要煲三小時半，否則湯寒涼，此湯下火又香甜。

PUERARIA, PORK AND DRIED OYSTER SOUP

Ingredients:

1⅓ lb pueraria
10 oz pork from knuckles
10 dried oysters
a slice ginger
2 stalks spring onion

Method:

1. Skin and wash pueraria. Cut into thick slices.

2. Add pork in boiling water and cook for 5 minutes. Take out and wash.
3. Soak dried oysters for 15 minutes and wash. Then soak in boiled water for ½ hour. Drains.
4. Saute ginger, spring onion and dried oyster with ½ tbsp oil. Add a cup of water and cook for a while. Dispose ginger and spring onion. Wash dried oyster to remove the grease.
5. Boil 10 cups of water, add pueraria, pork and dried oyster. Bring to the boil. Simmer for 3½–4 hours. Add salt.
6. Serve soup in bowl. The ingredients serve in plate and sprinkle on cooked oil and light soy.

(2)瘦肉、排骨同放入滾水中煮五
分鐘，取起洗淨。

(3)水九杯或適量煲滾，下瘦肉、
排骨、沙蟲、薑，再煲滾後，
慢火煲二小時半，熄火，待稍
冷，將湯倒出，以防煲底有
沙。取出排骨、瘦肉洗一洗
（免沙黏在肉上），沙蟲、薑不
要。

(4)排骨、瘦肉、湯再放回煲內煲
滾，落鹽調味，盛湯碗內上
桌。

註：

沙蟲可到海味店購買，據說對糖
尿病有食療作用，不管是否可
信，此湯老少皆宜，湯味特別鮮
美。

沙蟲煲瘦肉湯

用料：

瘦肉半斤，排骨四両(斬件)，沙
蟲乾一両半(沙蟲不是金魚吃的
沙蟲，是一種海產名稱)，薑一
片。

做法：

(1)沙蟲因有很多沙附在身上，首
先要除去沙。把沙蟲放焗爐慢
火焗十分鐘取出冷却後，將沙
拍去，洗淨，放落滾水中煮五
分鐘，取出洗淨。另一個方法
是將沙蟲放落鑊中，不落油，
用最慢火炒五至十分鐘，把沙
拍去。

LEAN PORK WITH DRIED SHA-CHUNG SOUP

Ingredients:
10 oz lean pork
5 oz spare ribs (chopped)
2 oz dried sha-chung
a slice ginger

Method:
1. As sand is usually found on Sha-chung, it is important to remove the sand first. Put Sha-chung in oven to bake for 10 minutes. Cool, shake off sand and wash. Cook in boiling water for 5 minutes, wash. Another alternative is to put Sha-chung in wok and fry without oil for 5–10 minutes. Shake off sand.

2. Put lean pork and spare ribs in boiling water to cook for 5 minutes. Wash.
3. Boil 9 cups of water. Add lean pork, spare ribs, Sha-chung and ginger. Bring to boil. Simmer for 2½ hours. When cool, pour soup out (to prevent sand from sticking to the bottom of pot). Take out spare ribs and lean pork, wash. Dispose Sha-chung and ginger.
4. Put spare ribs, lean pork and soup back into pot and boil again. Add salt to soup and serve in bowl.

靑紅蘿蔔生欖煲豬踭湯

用料：

靑蘿蔔、紅蘿蔔共一斤，生欖六個（又名靑欖，買不到免用，用無花果代替），豬踭十二両。

做法：

(1)靑蘿蔔、紅蘿蔔去皮洗淨切厚件。

(2)生欖洗淨。

(3)豬踭放落滾水中煮五分鐘，取起洗淨。

(4)水九杯或適量煲滾，把豬踭、靑紅蘿蔔、生欖放入煲滾後，慢火煲二小時。湯料上碟，淋上少許生抽熟油，湯加適量的鹽、生抽半湯匙調味，盛湯碗內，湯料及湯齊上桌。

註：

(1)生欖在生果檔、街邊小販都有賣。

(2)生欖有潤喉及去口氣之功效。

CARROT, GREEN TURNIP, OLIVE AND PORK SOUP

Ingredients:

1⅓ lb carrots and green turnips

6 olive

1 lb pork from knuckles

Method:
1. Skin carrots and green turnips. Cut into thick pieces.
2. Wash olive.
3. Put pork in boiling water to cook for 5 minutes. Take out and wash.
4. Boil 9 cups of water. Put in pork, carrots, turnips and olive. Bring to the boil and simmer for 2 hours. Serve ingredients in plate. Add salt and ½ tbsp light soy to soup and serve in bowl.

雪梨
銀耳煲排骨湯

用料：

雪梨三個，銀耳半両，南杏仁二湯匙，北杏仁數粒，排骨十二両（或用半斤豬蹄代替）。

做法：

(1)銀耳用清水浸二小時，洗淨撕成小朵，放落滾水中煮五分鐘，取起洗淨滴乾水。（銀耳出水，可除異味）。

(2)杏仁放落滾水中煮五分鐘，去衣洗淨。

(3)排骨放落滾水中煮五分鐘，取起洗淨。

(4)雪梨切去心洗淨，切厚件。

(5)水八杯或適量煲滾，放下排骨、銀耳、雪梨、杏仁煲滾後，慢火煲二小時，落鹽調味。

PEAR, DRIED WHITE FUNGUS AND SPARE RIBS SOUP

Ingredients:
3 pears
½ oz dried white fungus
2 tbsp almond
few bitter almond
1 lb spare ribs

Method:
1. Soak dried white fungus in water for 2 hours. Wash and tear into small pieces. Put into boiling water to cook for 5 minutes. Wash and drain.
2. Put almonds in boiling water and cook for 5 minutes. Remove the membrane and wash.
3. Put spare ribs in boiling water to cook for 5 minutes. Wash.
4. Remove the skin and core of pear. Cut into thick pieces.
5. Boil 8 cups of water. Put in spare ribs, white fungus, pear and almonds. Bring to the boil, then simmer for 2 hours. Season with salt.

栗子瑤柱排骨湯

用料：

瘦排骨十二両，栗子連殼四両，瑤柱半両，果皮八分一個(浸軟洗淨)。

做法：

(1)瑤柱洗淨用清水浸一小時。

(2)栗子連殼洗淨，要多洗幾次，因栗子殼有毛。

(3)排骨放落滾水中煮五分鐘，取起洗淨。

(4)水九杯或適量連果皮煲滾，加入排骨、瑤柱、栗子煲滾後，慢火煲二小時，加入適量的鹽及生抽半湯匙調味。

(5)栗子撈起去殼，可作零食。

註：

栗子連殼煲湯，因為栗子殼可作中藥用，有去痰火之功效。如用栗子肉煲湯，湯會變黑。

SPARE RIBS, CONPOY AND CHESTNUT SOUP

Ingredients:

1 lb lean spare ribs

6 oz chestnuts (with shells)

½ oz conpoy

$\frac{1}{8}$ dried tangerine peel (soaked and washed)

Method:

1. Wash conpoy and soak in water for an hour.
2. Wash chestnuts several times to remove hair on the shell.
3. Put spare ribs in boiling water and cook for 5 mintues. Wash.
4. Put dried tangerine peel in 9 cups of water. Bring to boil. Add spare ribs, conpoy and chestnuts. Simmer for 2 hours. Add salt and ½ tbsp light soy to soup.
5. Take out chestnuts and remove the shell.

玉竹豬肺湯

用料：

豬肺一個，豬蹍四両，玉竹二両（玉竹中藥店有賣），百合半両，無花果四個。

做法：

(1)玉竹、百合用清水浸半小時，洗淨滴乾水。

(2)把豬肺喉部套在水喉上，以水灌入肺內，待肺漲滿水後放在盆上，用手把肺內之水壓出；然後再用水灌入肺內，接着又壓出，用此方法，一直把豬肺洗至白色，此時肺內之污穢已洗淨。這是洗豬肺的方法。

(3)把豬肺切件，放入滾水中煮滾再煮五分鐘，取出洗淨滴乾。

(4)豬蹍放入滾水中煮五分鐘取出洗淨。

(5)水九杯或適量煲滾，加入豬蹍、豬肺、無花果、玉竹、百合煲滾後，慢火煲二小時半，加鹽調味。

註：

豬肺、玉竹、無花果、百合都有潤肺之功效。

POLYGONATUM WITH PIG LUNG SOUP

Ingredients:
1 pig lung
6 oz shin of pork
3 oz polygonatum
½ oz lily bulb
4 figs

Method:
1. Soak polygonatum and lily bulb for ½ hour. Wash and drain.

2. Link the bronchial tubes to the tap. Run water into the lungs. When it's inflated with water, press the water out. Repeat several times until the lung has turned white in color.
3. Slice pig lung and put into boiling water to cook for 5 mintues. Take out and wash.
4. Put pork steak in boiling water to cook for 5 minutes. Take out and wash.

5. Boil 9 cups of water. Add pork, pig lung, figs, polygonatum and lily bulb. Bring to boil, then simmer for 2½ hours. Season with salt.

眉豆
冬菇腳排骨湯

用料：

眉豆二両，冬菇腳三分一杯，瘦排骨十二両，紅棗六粒(去核)。

做法：

(1)眉豆、冬菇腳洗淨，用清水浸半小時，隔去水分。

(2)排骨斬件放落滾水中煮五分鐘，取起洗淨。

(3)水十杯或適量放入煲內煲滾，加入眉豆、冬菇腳、紅棗、排骨煲滾後，慢火再煲二小時，加入適量之鹽及生抽半湯匙調味。

註：

平日食冬菇時，把冬菇腳剪出留存。加入數隻雞腳同煲更好。

BROW BEAN, MUSHROOM TICK WITH SPARE RIBS SOUP

Ingredients:

3 oz brow bean

$\frac{1}{3}$ cup mushroom tick

1 lb lean spare ribs

6 dried red dates (stones removed)

Method:

1. Wash brow bean and mushroom ticks. Soak in water for ½ hour. Drain.
2. Chop and cook spare ribs in boiling water for 5 minutes. Wash.
3. Boil 10 cups of water. Add beans, mushroom ticks, dried red dates and spare ribs. Bring to boil. Simmer for 2 hours. Add salt and ½ tbsp light soy to season.

大豆芽菜排骨湯

用料：

大豆芽菜十二両，排骨半斤斬件，薑一片。

做法：

(1)大豆芽菜切去根洗淨滴乾水，用一湯匙油爆香薑及大豆芽菜，鏟起。

(2)排骨放落滾水中煮五分鐘，取起洗淨滴乾水。

(3)水六杯或適量煲滾，下排骨、大豆芽菜煲滾後，慢火煲一小時，加入鹽及古月粉少許、生抽半湯匙調味。

(4)湯料盛碟上，淋上少許生抽、熟油，湯盛湯碗內齊上桌。

註：

可以用大豆芽菜滾魷魚片湯，此湯能治春溫病，即是春夏間覺得頭暈暈，有少少頭痛。飲大豆芽菜魷魚片湯，便會精神爽利，這是民間療方。

SPARE RIBS WITH SOYA BEAN SPROUTS SOUP

Ingredients:
1 lb soya bean sprouts
10 oz spare ribs (chopped)
1 slice ginger

Method:
1. Remove the roots of soya bean

sprouts. Wash and drain. Saute ginger and soy bean sprouts with 1 tbsp oil.
2. Put spare ribs in boiling water to cook for 5 minutes. Wash and drain.
3. Boil 6 cups of water. Add spare ribs, soya bean sprouts. Bring to boil and simmer for an hour.

Season with salt, a pinch of pepper and ½ tbsp light soy.
4. Serve ingredients in plate, sprinkle on cooked oil and light soy. Serve soup in bowl.

冬蟲草煲豬腰瘦肉湯

用料：

冬蟲草半両或適量，豬腰一隻，豬睜四両，豬橫脷一條，薑一片，酒一湯匙。

做法：

(1)豬腰切開邊，起去白筋，加梳打粉四分一茶匙、水一湯匙，醃二小時，洗去梳打粉味。（用梳打粉醃後多洗數次，可以除去豬腰之異味）

(2)瘦肉、豬腰、橫脷放落滾水中煮五分鐘，取出洗淨。

(3)水八杯或適量煲滾，下冬蟲草、豬腰、瘦肉、橫脷、薑、酒煲滾後，慢火煲二小時半。湯料切件盛碟上，湯加適量的鹽及生抽半湯匙調味，盛湯碗內一齊上桌。

註：

此湯補腎虧，如夜間小便頻密，多飲幾次有食療作用，而且此湯不肥膩又正氣。

CHINESE CORDYCEPS, LEAN PORK AND PIG KIDNEY SOUP

Ingredients:
½ oz Chinese cordyceps
1 pig kidney
6 oz shin of pork
1 pig midriff
a slice ginger

1 tbsp wine

Method:

1. Halve pig kidney and remove fatty cores. Marinate with ¼ tsp soda, 1 tbsp water for 2 hours. Wash to remove the soda.
2. Put pork, pig kidney and pig midriff into boiling water to cook for 5 minutes. Wash.
3. Boil 8 cups of water. Add Chinese cordyceps, pig kidney, pork, pig midriff, ginger and wine. Bring to boil and then simmer for 3½ hours. Chop up the ingredients and serve in plate. Season the soup with salt and ½ tbsp light soy. Serve in bowl.

白菜仔滾肉片湯

用料：
白菜仔四両，冬菇四隻，枚頭肉三両，薑一片。

醃料：
生抽半湯匙，生粉一茶匙，油半湯匙。

做法：
(1)冬菇浸軟去腳。

(2)白菜仔洗淨滴乾水。

(3)枚頭肉切薄片，加醃料醃十分鐘，放落滾水中灼至將熟撈起，水不要。

(4)水四杯或適量，薑一片，冬菇及油半湯匙同煲滾，加入白菜仔煲焾，下肉片煲熟，加入鹽調味，將湯料上碟，湯盛湯碗內，齊上枱。

註：
可用其他蔬菜代替白菜仔，例如菠菜、豆苗、冬瓜、節瓜。

WHITE CABBAGE WITH PORK SLICE SOUP

Ingredients:
6 oz white cabbage
4 black mushrooms
4 oz pork loin
a slice ginger

Seasoning:
½ tbsp light soy

1 tsp corn flour
½ tbsp oil

Method:

1. Soak mushrooms and trim.
2. Wash white cabbage Drain.
3. Cut pork loin into thick slices. Marinate with seasoning for 10 minutes. Blanch in hot water. Dispose the water.
4. Boil 4 cups of water. Add ginger, mushrooms and ½ tbsp oil. Bring to boil. Put in white cabbage. Cook until it's tender. Add pork loin and cook until it's tender. Season with salt. Serve the ingredients in plate and soup in bowl.

一茶匙，水半湯匙醃一至二小時（此法能使豬膶嫩滑），洗去梳打粉味。抹乾水，加醃料醃十分鐘，放落將滾之水中灼至將熟撈起，用清水冲洗。

(5)水五杯或適量（可用煲粉腸的湯），加入鹹酸菜、粉腸煮滾，再煮片刻，落豬膶煮熟後，加入芹菜及半湯匙油，落鹽調味。加少許辣油，便成酸辣湯了。

註：

此湯可以加入肉片、豬腰片、煲脸的豬肚切件，稱為豬雜湯。

鹹菜粉腸豬膶湯

用料：

鹹酸菜四両，豬粉腸四両，豬膶（豬肝）二両，中國芹菜一小棵（無芹菜季節，用芫荽代替）。

醃料：

麻油、古月粉少許，生抽半湯匙，生粉一茶匙，油半湯匙。

做法：

(1)芹菜去葉洗淨切短度。

(2)鹹酸菜洗淨（多洗幾次以減去鹹味，無須浸水）揸乾水，切小片。

(3)將一粒蒜肉放入粉腸一端，用手慢慢向另一端推出（蒜肉能把腸內的污穢通出），洗淨。加入適量之水及薑一片煲滾，慢火煲脸，約需四十分鐘，取起粉腸切件。

(4)豬膶切薄片，加梳打粉四分之

PIG CHITTERLINGS, PIG LIVER AND PRESERVED MUSTARD SOUP

Ingredients:
5 oz preserved mustard
5 oz pig chitterlings
3 oz pig liver
1 stalk Chinese celery

Seasoning:
pinch of sesame oil
pinch of pepper
½ tbsp light soy
1 tsp cornflour
½ tbsp oil.

Method:
1. Remove leaves of celery. Section.
2. Wash preserved mustard. (Wash several times to remove its saltiness, there's no need to soak in water). Squeeze out water and cut into little pieces.

3. Put a piece of garlic into one end of chitterlings and push to another end (garlic can remove the dirty substances of chitterlings). Wash. Put in boiling water with a slice of ginger. Simmer for 40 minutes unitil chitterlings are tender. Chop up.

4. Cut pork liver into thick slices. Add ¼ tsp soda and ½ tbsp water to marinate for 1 to 2 hours. Wash away the soda. Wipe dry and marinate with seasoning for 10 minutes. Blanch in boiling water, then wash under running water.

5. Put 5 cups of water in pot, add preserved mustard and chitterlings. Bring to boil and cook for a while. Put in pork liver until its tender, then add celery and ½ tbsp oil. Season with salt. Add some chilli oil as sour and hot soup.

生熟薏米
煲豬小肚湯

用料：

豬小肚三個(或用豬肚一個)，瘦肉四両，生熟薏米共一両(在中藥店、雜貨店有賣)，枝竹一両半，馬蹄六隻(去皮)，紅蘿蔔一小隻(去皮切件)。

做法：

(1)生熟薏米放落滾水中煮五分鐘(以去膠質)，撈起用清水沖洗，滴乾水。

(2)枝竹洗淨剪短度。

(3)豬小肚切開，洗去異味。(用番石榴葉或番石榴揸爛，用以搓擦豬小肚數分鐘，再用清水沖洗，這樣可以把豬肚、豬大腸、牛雜的異味除去)

(4)將豬小肚和瘦肉放落滾水中煮五分鐘，取起洗淨，豬小肚白鑊煎一煎鏟起再洗(白鑊即是不下油)。

(5)水八杯或適量煲滾，將豬小肚、瘦肉、生熟薏米、紅蘿蔔、枝竹、馬蹄放入煲滾，慢火煲二小時半，加鹽調味。豬小肚切件，與湯盛湯碗內。

PIG BLADDER WITH PEARL BARLEY SOUP

Ingredients:
3 pig bladders
6 oz lean pork
1½ oz pearl barley
2 oz dried beancurd sticks
6 water chestnuts (shells removed)
a small carrot (skinned and sliced)

Method:
1. Boil pearl barley for 5 minutes. Wash and drain.

2. Wash dried beancurd sticks and cut into short pieces.
3. Paunch bladders and wash to remove the smell. (Use leaves of guava or crush of guava to rub onto bladders for a few minutes, then wash).
4. Put bladders and lean pork into boiling water to boil for 5 minutes. Take out and wash. Fry bladders in a work without oil, then wash.
5. Boil 8 cups of water, add bladders, lean pork, pearl barley, carrots, dried beancurd sticks and water chestnut. Bring to boil. Simmer for 2½ hours. Add salt to season. Slice bladders and serve together with the soup in bowl.

五分鐘,取起排骨再洗淨滴乾水。

(2)當歸、八角、薑、蒜頭、香茅最好用紗布包好。

(3)水八杯或適量煲滾,落排骨、當歸、八角、薑、蒜頭、香茅煲滾後,慢火煲出味,約需一小時。取起當歸、八角、薑、香茅、蒜頭不要,加入調味攪勻。試味,湯和排骨同上窩,便成香噴噴的排骨茶了。

註:

(1)香茅可到賣椰汁的香料店買。

(2)星洲的排骨茶很馳名,本茶譜不冠以星洲之名的原因,就是採用材料不盡同,減少了一些藥材和香料,更適合香港家庭口味,而又不失其特色。

(3)所用材料有療效,當歸:調順經血;蒜:通便殺菌;八角:除寒溫,通順行血;薑:袪風;香茅:袪寒,有辛香味。

排骨茶

用料:

瘦排骨一斤,當歸半兩切片,八角二粒,香茅一枝拍扁,薑一片,蒜頭一個約重一兩(不去衣)。

調味:

生抽二湯匙,老抽半湯匙,鹽一茶匙或適量。

做法:

(1)排骨斬件洗淨,放落滾水中煮

SPARE RIBS TEA

Ingredients:
$1\frac{1}{3}$ lb spare ribs
½ oz chiretta (sliced)
2 star anise
1 parang leaf
a slice ginger
1 garlic (with membrane)

Seasoning:
½ tbsp light soy
½ tbsp dark soy
1 tsp salt

Method:

1. Chop and wash spare ribs. Put into boiling water to cook for 5 minutes. Wash again and drain.

2. Wrap chiretta, star anise, ginger, garlic and parang leaf with a piece of cloth.

3. Boil 8 cups water. Add spare ribs, chiretta, star anise, ginger, garlic and parang leaf. Bring to boil and simmer for an hour. Dispose chiretta, star anise, ginger, parang leaf and garlic. Add seasoning and taste. Serve in bowl.

枸杞窩蛋豬膶湯

用料：

枸杞半斤，豬膶三両，鷄蛋二隻（或用六隻鵪鶉蛋）。

醃料：

生抽二茶匙，麻油、古月粉少許，生粉一茶匙半，油一湯匙。

做法：

(1) 豬膶切薄片，加梳打粉四分一茶匙、水半湯匙醃一至二小時（此法使豬肝嫩滑）。洗去梳打粉味，抹乾水，加醃料醃十分鐘，放落將滾之水中灼至將熟，取起用清水洗。

(2) 枸杞洗淨，把葉摘下盛脊箕內。

(3) 枸杞莖折短放入煲內，加入水五杯或適量煲滾，慢火煲出味，約需十五分鐘。

(4) 取起莖不要，加入油一湯匙、鹽適量，並放下枸杞葉。將鷄蛋去殼，逐隻倒入湯內（蛋不要拂匀），待蛋白凝固後再下第二隻蛋，蛋落完後，豬膶也放入湯內，熟後即成。

MEDLAK, PIG LIVER WITH EGG SOUP

Ingredients:
10 oz medlar
4 oz pig liver
2 eggs (or 6 quail eggs)

Seasoning:
2 tsp light soy
pinch of sesame oil
pinch of pepper
1½ tsp cornflour
1 tbsp oil

Method:

1. Cut pig liver into thin slices. Marinate with ¼ tsp soda and ½ tbsp water for 1 to 2 hours. Wash away the soda, wipe dry and add seasoning to marinate for 10 minutes. Blanch in boiling water. Take out and wash with cold water.

2. Wash medlar. Remove the stems of medlar.

3. Section stem of medlar and put into pot. Add 5 cups of water and bring to the boil. Simmer for about 15 minutes.

4. Dispose the stem, add 1 tbsp oil and pinch of salt. Add leaves of medlar, then eggs one by one (with the shells removed, but not whisked). Put in pig liver and simmer until its fully cooked.

韭黃肉絲燴髮菜

用料：

髮菜半兩，肉眼三兩，冬菇半兩，冬筍肉二兩，韭黃一兩切短度，薑二片，葱二條，酒半湯匙，上湯五杯半（可用罐頭清雞湯）。

醃料：

生抽半湯匙，生粉一茶匙，油一湯匙。

獻：

水半杯，粟粉二湯匙，麻油、古月粉少許，生抽一湯匙，鹽、糖各三分一茶匙。

做法：

(1) 冬菇浸軟揸乾水，剪去腳切絲。

(2) 冬筍肉放落滾水中煮十五分鐘，取出用清水浸冷，切絲。（用罐頭筍只要洗一洗便可切絲，然後揸乾水）

(3) 肉眼切絲，加醃料醃十分鐘，放落將滾之水中灼至將熟撈起（或泡嫩油）。

(4) 髮菜用清水浸十分鐘，洗淨揸乾水。

(5) 薑二片、葱二條、酒半湯匙、油一湯匙、水三杯或適量煮滾，放下髮菜煮五分鐘，取起揸乾水。

(6) 上湯五杯半，加髮菜煮滾再煮片刻，取起髮菜放湯碗內剪短。

(7) 把冬菇、筍絲放落煮過髮菜之上湯內煮滾，再煮片刻，下肉絲煮熟，埋稀獻，下韭黃兜勻，倒在盛髮菜之湯碗內。

FAT-CHOI, YELLOW CHIVES WITH PORK SLICE SOUP

Ingredients:
½ oz Fat-choi
5 oz pork loin
½ oz black mushroom
3 oz winter bamboo shoots
1½ oz yellow chives (sectioned)
2 slices ginger
2 stalks spring onion
½ tbsp wine
5½ cups superior stock (canned chicken broth can be used)

Seasoning:
½ tbsp light soy
1 tsp cornflour
1 tbsp oil

Sauce:
½ cup water
2 tbsp cornflour
pinch of sesame oil
pinch of pepper
1 tbsp light soy
$\frac{1}{3}$ tsp salt
$\frac{1}{3}$ tsp sugar

Method:

1. Soak black mushrooms and squeeze out excess water. Trim and slice.

2. Put bamboo shoots into boiling water to cook for 15 minutes, then soak in water, slice. (When canned bamboo shoots are used, wash and slice, then squeeze out excess water)

3. Slice pork loin, marinate with seasoning for 10 minutes and blanch in boiling water.

4. Soak Fat-choi for 10 minutes, wash and squeeze out excess water.

5. Put 2 slices ginger, 2 stalks spring onion, ½ tbsp wine and 1 tbsp oil in 3 cups of water. Bring to the boil. Add Fat-choi and cook for another 5 minutes. Take Fat-choi out and squeeze out excess water.

6. Add Fat-choi to 5½ cups stock. Bring to the boil and cook for a while. Take out Fat-choi and put in bowl, cut into short sections with a pair of scissors.

7. Put mushrooms and bamboo shoots into the stock. Bring to boil and cook for a while. Add pork slices and cook until its tender. Put in sauce and chives. Stir well. Serve in bowl together with Fat-choi.

生滾牛肉湯

用料：

牛肉三両，生菜六両，薑絲一湯匙。

醃料：

生抽半湯匙，糖四分一茶匙，生粉一茶匙，水半湯匙，油半湯匙。

調味：

水四杯或適量，麻油、古月粉少許，鹽四分三茶匙或適量。

做法：

(1)生菜洗淨切粗條。

(2)牛肉切橫紋薄片，加梳打粉四分一茶匙、水一湯匙，醃一至二小時（如牛肉軟脸就無須醃梳打粉）。洗去梳打粉味，抹乾水，加醃料醃十分鐘，放落將滾之水中灼至將熟撈起，水不要。

(3)用一湯匙油，爆薑絲，下調味煮滾，下生菜及牛肉，煮熟後便可。生菜牛肉盛碟上，湯盛湯碗內一齊上桌。

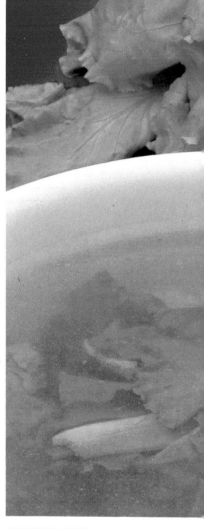

BEEF SOUP

Ingredients:
4 oz beef
8 oz lettuce
1 tbsp ginger (shredded)

Seasoning (1):
½ tbsp light soy
¼ tsp sugar
1 tsp cornflour
½ tbsp water
½ tbsp oil

Seasoning (2):
4 cups water
pinch of sesame oil
pinch of pepper
¾ tbsp oil

Method:
1. Wash lettuce and shred.
2. Thinly slice the beef straight across the grain. Add ¼ tsp soda and 1 tbsp water to marinate for 1–2 hours. After that, wash the beef to remove the soda. Wipe dry and marinate with seasoning (1) for 10 minutes. Blanch in boiling water.
3. Saute ginger with 1 tbsp oil. Add seasoning (2). Bring to boil. Add lettuce and beef, to cook until it's tender. Serve lettuce and beef in plate and soup in bowl.

牛肉茶

用料：

牛肉三両，薑一小片，西芹半條切短度（增加香味，不要也可以）。

做法：

(1)牛肉洗淨抹乾水，剁幼或用碎肉機攪碎，加清水一又四分一杯，浸一至二小時，浸時放入雪櫃。

(2)將牛肉及浸牛肉之水倒入煲內，加入薑及西芹煲滾，慢火煲出味，約十分鐘，將渣隔去，湯再煲滾，落鹽調味。食時可加入數滴鮮露豉油，以增鮮味。

註：

牛膶、豬膶也可以用同樣方法做，稱為牛膶茶或豬膶茶，既簡單又補身。

BEEF TEA

Ingredients:
4 oz beef
a slice ginger
½ stalk sectioned celery

Method:
1. Wash beef and wipe dry. Mince. Soak in 1¼ cup water for 1–2 hours. When soak, keep in a refrigerator.
2. Put beef together with the water in which beef has been soaked into pot, add ginger and celery. Bring to boil. Simmer for 10 minutes. Dispose the ingredients. Bring to the boil again. Season with salt and light soy.

淮山
杞子煲牛蹎湯

用料：

牛蹎十二両，淮山半両，杞子二
湯匙，龍眼肉乾一湯匙半，薑一
片。

做法：

(1)牛蹎切厚片，放落滾水中煮五
　分鐘，取起洗淨。

(2)水八杯煲滾，下牛蹎、淮山、
　杞子、龍眼肉、薑煲滾後，慢
　火煲三小時，加鹽及生抽半湯
　匙調味。

註：

可以用水魚或羊肉一斤代替牛
蹎。

BEEF WITH YAM AND MEDLAR SOUP

Ingredients:
1 lb shin of beef
½ oz yam
2 tbsp medlar (dried seeds)

1½ tbsp dried longan (shell removed)
a slice ginger

Method:

1. Thickly slice shin of beef. Put in boiling water to cook for 5 minutes. Take out and wash.
2. Boil 8 cups of water, add beef, yam, medlar, longan and ginger. Bring to the boil. Simmer for 3 hours. Add salt and ½ tbsp light soy to season.

清補涼
煲牛雙連湯

用料：

牛雙連一斤（即牛胃），豬蹄四兩，清補涼一包，約重三兩（內有淮山、薏米、蓮子、芡實、百合、圓肉、玉竹）。

做法：

(1)牛雙連買時請賣者起去黑衣，黑衣不起也可以的，只是不美觀。

(2)牛雙連、豬蹄放落滾水中煮五分鐘，取起洗淨。

(3)水九杯或適量煲滾，將牛雙連、豬蹄、清補涼放入煲滾，慢火再煲二小時。豬蹄、牛雙連切件上碟，湯加適量的鹽及半湯匙生抽調味，盛湯碗內一起上桌。

註：

此湯老少四季皆宜，可去小孩「積滯」。

CHING-PO-LEUNG WITH OX TRIPE SOUP

Ingredients:

$1\frac{1}{3}$ lb ox tripe

5 oz shin of pork

4 oz Ching-po-leung (includes yam, pearl barley, lotus-nut, fox-nut,

dried lily bulb, dried longan and polygonatum)

Method:

1. Remove the black membrane of ox tripe (This can be done by the butcher).

2. Put ox tripe and shin of pork in boiling water to cook for 5 minutes. Take out and wash.

3. Boil 9 cups of water. Add ox tripe, pork and Ching-po-leung. Bring to boil, then simmer for 2 hours. Slice pork and ox tripe, serve in plate, Add salt and ½ tbsp light soy to soup. Serve in bowl.

蓮藕煲牛腩湯

用料：

蓮藕十二両至一斤，牛腩一斤（最好坑腩，較瘦），果皮六分一個（浸軟洗淨），紅棗六粒（去核），薑一片。

做法：

(1)蓮藕去皮洗淨。

(2)牛腩放落滾水中煮十分鐘，取起洗淨。

(3)水十杯或酌量，加果皮煲滾，下蓮藕、牛腩、紅棗、薑，煲滾後，慢火煲至牛腩腍，約需三小時。蓮藕、牛腩切件上碟。湯加鹽及生抽一湯匙調味，放上少許葱碎增香味，湯盛湯碗內齊上桌。

註：

把煲過湯的蓮藕及牛腩，加以調味炆片刻，便成為一欵菜式，請參閱李曾鵬展食譜「煲仔菜」之「蓮藕牛踭煲」及「柱侯牛腩煲」。

BRISKET OF BEEF WITH LOTUS ROOTS SOUP

Ingredients:

1 lb lotus roots
$1\frac{1}{3}$ lb brisket of beef
$\frac{1}{6}$ dried tangerine peel (soaked and cleaned)
6 dried red dates (stones removed)
a slice ginger

Method:
1. Remove the skin of lotus roots. Wash.
2. Put brisket of beef into boiling water and cook for 10 minutes. Take out and wash.
3. Boil 10 cups of water with tangerine peel. Add lotus roots, beef, dried red dates and ginger. Bring to boil and simmer for 3 hours until beef in tender. Slice lotus roots and beef. Serve in plate. Add salt and 1 tbsp light soy to soup. Sprinkle on shredded spring onion and serve in bowl.

牛骨雜菜湯

用料：

洋葱一個(約三兩)，西芹一條切短度，椰菜半斤，番茄三隻，甘筍一小隻(切粗而短條)，牛踭六兩(切厚件)，牛脊骨十二兩至一斤(買時請賣者將牛骨切開一節節)，蒜肉四粒(連皮)，茄汁四湯匙，太白斯高辣汁適量。

做法：

(1)牛脊骨、牛踭同放落滾水中煮十分鐘，取起洗淨，滴乾水。

(2)洋葱去衣洗淨切絲。

(3)椰菜洗淨切粗條。

(4)番茄去核洗淨切件。

(5)下油二湯匙爆香洋葱、西芹、番茄、椰菜、蒜肉、茄汁。

(6)水十二杯或適量煲滾，將牛骨、牛踭及以爆過的雜菜、甘筍加入，煲滾後慢火煲二小時半至三小時，牛骨、蒜肉取起不要，加鹽及古月粉調味，食時可隨各人喜愛加入太白斯高辣汁，酸酸辣辣更好味。

(7)如果想做雜菜羹，此分量可用約四湯匙粟粉加水開勻，慢慢倒下湯內攪勻，煮滾便可。

OX BONES AND VEGET-ABLE SOUP

Ingredients:
1 onion (approximately 4 oz)
1 stalk celery (sectioned)
10 oz cabbage
3 tomatoes
1 small carrot (cut in short and thick stripes)
8 oz shin of beef (slice thickly)

1 lb ox bones
4 garlics
4 tbsp tomato ketchup
Dash of Tabesco

Method:

1. Put ox bones and beef in boiling water and boil for 10 minutes. Wash and drain.
2. Remove skin of onion and shred.
3. Wash cabbage and shred.
4. Remove the seeds of tomato, wash and slice.
5. Saute onion, celery, tomato, cabbage, garlic and tomato with 2 tbsp oil.
6. Boil 12 cups of wates. Put in bones, beef and the vegetables. Bring to boil, then simmer for 2½–3 hours. Dispose the bones and garlic. Season with salt and pepper. Serve with Tabesco.

鹹檸檬燉羊肉湯

用料：

羊髀肉一斤（斬件），鹹檸檬半個（在雜貨店或醬園購買），杞子二湯匙，薑一片，酒半湯匙，白蘿蔔一小隻，滾水六杯。

做法：

(1)蘿蔔洗淨切件，加入清水約五杯煮滾，下羊肉煮十分鐘，取起洗淨。（羊肉用蘿蔔出水，可除去羶味，如不怕羶味，可以不用蘿蔔出水，只用滾水便可）

(2)鹹檸檬取去核洗淨，因核有苦澀味。

(3)將羊肉、鹹檸檬、杞子、薑、酒、滾水放燉盅內，用密蓋燉四小時，落鹽調味，原盅上桌。

註：

羊肉以黑草羊最好，皮黑色的稱黑草羊。

MUTTON WITH SALTED LEMON SOUP

Ingredient:
1 1/3 lb leg of lamb
1/2 salted lemon
2 tbsp medlar (dried seeds)
a slice ginger

½ tbsp wine
1 turnip
6 cups boiling water

Method:

1. Wash and shred turnip. Add in 5 cups of water in pot and bring to boil. Put in mutton and cook for 10 minutes. Take out and wash. Dispose the turnip.

2. Remove the seeds of salted lemon.

3. Put mutton, salted lemon, medlar, ginger, wine and boilding water in a steaming pot. Simmer for 4 hours. Season with salt. Serve in pot.

魚、海鮮

豆腐滾魚頭湯

用料：

大魚頭一個約重半斤（切開二邊），芥菜四両，板豆腐一件（約三吋丁方），薑一片。

醃料：

古月粉少許，鹽三分一茶匙。

做法：

(1)芥菜洗淨切短度，滴乾水。

(2)豆腐洗淨切為二件。

(3)大魚頭加醃料搽勻，醃十五分鐘，抹乾水，用二湯匙油煎至微黃色鏟起。

(4)水四杯半或適量，加薑一片在鑊中煮滾，落魚頭、豆腐煮滾，用中火滾十至十五分鐘，落芥菜煮熟。湯料盛碟上，淋上生抽熟油，湯加鹽調味盛湯碗內，一同上桌。

註：

(1)除了用大魚頭外，也可用石斑頭、青衣頭、鱸魚頭、鮸魚尾或沙鯭魚。

(2)除了用芥菜，也可用白菜、黃芽白或西洋菜。

(3)俗語有說「千滾豆腐萬滾魚」，即是說豆腐和魚滾湯，時間煮久了也是好吃的。

FISH HEAD WITH BEAN-CORD SOUP

Ingredients:

1 fish head (about 10 oz) (halve)
5 oz leaf mustard
1 beancurd (approximately 3″ square)
a slice ginger

Seasoning:

pinch of pepper

¹⁄₃ tsp salt

Method:
1. Wash and section leaf mustard. Drain.
2. Wash beancurd and halve.
3. Rub fish head with seasoning and marinate for 15 minutes. Wipe dry. Shallow fry with 2 tbsp oil until slightly brown.
4. Boil 4½ cups of water together with a slice of ginger. Add fish head and beancurd. Bring to boil, simmer for about 10 to 15 minutes. Put in leaf mustard and cook for a while. Serve ingredients in plate, sprinkle on light soy and cooked oil. Add salt to soup and serve in bowl.

潺菜豆腐
滾大眼魚湯

用料：

潺菜半斤，豆腐一件（三吋丁方），大眼魚一條重半斤（又稱剝皮魚，買時請賣者剝皮），薑一片。

做法：

(1)潺菜洗淨摘短度。

(2)豆腐洗淨切為二件。

(3)魚洗淨抹乾水，加入古月粉少許，鹽半茶匙醃十五分鐘，抹乾水，用二湯匙油煎至兩面微黃色鏟起。

(4)水五杯半適量煮滾，下魚、豆腐、薑，冚密蓋煮滾，用中火煮約十五分鐘，落潺菜煮熟，下鹽調味。湯料盛碟上，湯盛湯碗內齊上桌。

註：

(1)據說此湯可去煙蹟，對吸煙的人有食療作用。豆腐滾魚湯特別鮮美，營養豐富。

(2)除大眼魚外，可用紅衫魚、鯇魚尾。

CEYLON SPINACH, BEANCORD AND FISH SOUP

Ingredients:

10 oz ceylon spinach
1 beancurd (3″ square)
1 Tai-Gum-Yu (skin removed)
a slice ginger

Method:

1. Wash and section ceylon spinach.
2. Wash and halve beancurd.
3. Wash fish and wipe dry. Marinate with a pinch of pepper and ½ tsp salt for 15 minutes. Wipe dry. Shallow fry with 2 tbsp oil until lightly brown.
4. Boil 5 cups of water. Put in fish, beancurd, ginger and cook with the lid on. Simmer for 15 minutes. Add ceylon spinach and cook for a while. Season with salt. Serve ingredients in plate and soup in bowl.

蓴菜魚丸湯

用料：

蓴菜一樽（蓴菜盛在玻璃瓶內，瓶中有水浸着），鯪魚肉四両（不要皮），上湯四杯。

獻：

粟粉一又三分一湯匙，水三分一杯。

魚丸調味：

水六湯匙，鹽三分一茶匙，古月粉少許，生粉半湯匙。

做法：

(1)魚肉剁至極幼，加魚丸調味攪至起膠，做成魚丸，放在已搽油之碟上，蒸七分鐘至熟。

(2)蓴菜倒在筲箕上洗一洗，滴乾水。

(3)把上湯煮滾，下蓴菜、魚丸煮滾，慢火再煮七至十分鐘，埋獻，下鹽調味，放熟油（或粟米油）半湯匙，盛湯碗上桌。

註：

蓴菜是杭州西湖特產，此菜只宜滾湯，在上海店有賣。

FISH BALL WITH BRASENIA PURPUREA SOUP

Ingredients:

1 bottle of brasenia purpurea (edible water plant)

5 oz dace (skin removed)

4 cups superior stock

Sauce:

$1\frac{1}{3}$ tbsp cornflour

$\frac{1}{3}$ cup water

Seasoning for fish ball:
6 tbsp water
⅓ tsp salt
pinch of pepper
½ tbsp cornflour

Method:

1. Mince dace, add seasoning and stir well till it turns sticky. Roll into fish balls. Put on top of plate that was rubbed with oil. Steam for 7 minutes.

2. Wash brasenia purpurea, drain.
3. Boil stock, add brasenia purpurea and fish ball. Bring to boil. Reduce heat and simmer for 7—10 minutes. Put in sauce and salt. Add ½ tbsp cooked oil (or corn oil). Serve in bowl.

冬瓜海蜒湯

用料：

冬瓜一斤，海蜒一両半(海蜒又稱丁香魚仔乾)。

調味：

鹽三分一茶匙或適量，古月粉少許，油半湯匙。

做法：

(1)冬瓜去皮去囊洗淨切件。

(2)海蜒洗淨滴乾水。

(3)水五杯煲滾，下海蜒、冬瓜煲滾後，慢火再煲半小時，待冬瓜腍後，加調味即成。

註：

海蜒在雜貨店稱爲丁香魚仔，在南貨店稱海蜒。

DRIED SEA MILLIPEDE WITH WHITE GOURD SOUP

Ingredients:

1$\frac{1}{3}$ lb white gourd

2 oz dried sea millipede

Seasoning:
$1/3$ tsp salt
pinch of pepper
$1/2$ tbsp oil

Method:
1. Remove the skin and seeds of white gourd. Section.
2. Wash and drain dried millipede.
3. Boil 5 cups of water. Add dried millipede and white gourd. Bring to boil. Simmer for $1/2$ hour until gourd is tender. Add seasoning.

紫菜魚皮羹

用料：

沙魚皮乾二両，中國火腿半両切絲，紫菜半両，雞胸肉四両，果皮半個(浸軟切絲)。

煨魚皮用料：

薑二片，葱二條，酒一湯匙，水三杯，油半湯匙。

調味：

上湯七杯(可用罐頭清雞湯)，麻油、古月粉少許，鹽一茶匙，糖半茶匙，生抽一湯匙。

獻：

粟粉五湯匙，水半杯，老抽半湯匙。

做法：

(1)沙魚皮加入蓋過面二吋之清水浸二小時，倒落煲內煲滾後，慢火煲二十分鐘，熄火，待冷取起，洗淨，因沙魚皮有很多沙。

(2)煮滾煨魚皮用料，下魚皮煮五分鐘，撈起滴乾水。

(3)雞胸肉切絲，加生粉一茶匙，油一湯匙撈勻，放落將滾之水中灼到將熟撈起。或泡嫩油。

(4)紫菜剪粗絲，放落白鑊中炒香，以去腥味。(白鑊即是不下油)

(5)下油一湯匙，落調味、果皮、紫菜、魚皮、火腿煮滾，埋獻，下雞絲兜勻煮滾，盛湯碗內上桌。

註：

沙魚皮在海味店購買。沙魚皮是切成絲的，所以買回來不用切。沙魚皮營養豐富，價錢便宜，味滑而鮮。

SHARK'S SKIN WITH LAVER SOUP

Ingredients:

3 oz dried shark's skin
½ oz Chinese ham (shredded)
½ oz laver
5 oz chicken breast
½ dried tangerine peel (soaked and shredded)

Ingredients for stewing shark's skin:

2 slices ginger
2 stalks spring onion
3 cups water
½ tbsp oil

Seasoning:

7 cups superior stock (canned chicken broth can be used)
pinch of sesame oil
pinch of pepper
1 tsp salt
½ tsp sugar
1 tbsp light soy

Sauce:

5 tbsp cornflour

½ cup water
½ tbsp dark soy

Method:

1. Soak shark's skin for 2 hours, that there will be enough water to cover shark's skin. Bring to boil. Simmer for 20 minutes. Take out when cool. Wash.

2 Boil the ingredients for stewing shark's skin. Put in shark's skin and cook for 5 minutes. Drain.

3. Shred chicken breast. Marinate with 1 tsp cornflour and 1 tbsp oil. Blanch in boiling water.

4. Shred laver. Fry in a dried wok to remove the smell.

5. Boil seasoning together with 1 tbsp oil, tangerine peel, laver, shark's skin and ham. Bring to boil. Add sauce, then chicken. Stir well. Bring to boil again and serve in bowl.

粉葛煲鯪魚湯

用料：

粉葛一斤，鯪魚二條約重十二両
至一斤，赤小豆二両，蜜棗四
粒，果皮四分一個(浸軟洗淨)。

做法：

(1)鯪魚劏後洗淨抹乾水，用二湯
　匙油煎至兩面皆黃色鏟起。

(2)粉葛批去皮，洗淨切厚件。

(3)赤小豆洗淨。

(4)水十杯或適量，放下果皮煲
　滾，下鯪魚、粉葛、赤小豆、
　蜜棗煲滾後，慢火煲三小時半
　至四小時。鯪魚、粉葛盛碟
　上，湯加鹽調味盛湯碗內，魚
　及湯齊上桌。

註：

(1)粉葛煲湯最少要煲三小時半，
　煲的時間短，飲後覺寒涼。

(2)鯪魚粉葛湯可去骨火。

DACE WITH ROOT OF PUERARIA SOUP

Ingredients:
$1^{1}/_{3}$ lb root of pueraria
2 dace (about 1 lb)
3 oz red peal bean
4 preserved dates

¼ dried tangerine peel (soaked and cleaned)

Method:

1. Scale, gut and wash dace. Wipe dry. Fry with 2 tbsp oil until both sides are just brown.
2. Remove the skin of pueraria, wash and section.
3. Wash red peal bean.
4. Boil 10 cups of water with tangerine peel together. Add dace, pueraria, red peal bean and dates. Bring to boil. Simmer for 3½—4 hours. Serve dace and pueraria in plate. Add salt to soup and serve in bowl.

紅棗煲生魚湯

用料：
生魚一條，重十二両，黑豆二
両，紅棗十粒去核，薑一片，果
皮四分一個(浸軟洗淨)。

做法：
(1)黑豆白鑊炒至豆殼裂開，鏟起
　洗淨滴乾水。(白鑊即不下油)
(2)生魚去內臟去鱗洗淨抹乾水，
　用一湯匙油煎至兩面微黃色鏟
　起。
(3)水八杯或適量，連果皮同放煲
　內煲滾後，加入生魚、紅棗、
　薑、黑豆煲滾後慢火煲二小時
　半，加鹽及生抽半湯匙調味。

註：
可用塘蝨魚、鯉魚代替生魚。

SAN-YU WITH DRIED RED DATES SOUP

Ingredients:
1 San-yu (about 1 lb) (fresh water fish)
3 oz black beans
10 dried red dates (stones removed)
a slice ginger

¼ dried tangerine peel (soaked and
cleaned)

Method:

1. Fry black beans in a dried wok
   until the shells cracked. Take
   out, wash and drain.
2. Scale, gut and wash the fish.
   Wipe dry. Fry with 1 tbsp oil
   until both sides are slightly
   brown.
3. Boil 8 cups of water together
   with tangerine peel. Add San-yu
   dried red dates, ginger and black
   beans. Bring to boil, simmer
   for 2 hours. Add salt and ½ tbsp
   light soy to soup. Serve in bowl.

紅蘿蔔
煲石九公湯

用料：

細石九公一斤，紅蘿蔔一斤，紅棗十粒去核，薑一片。

做法：

(1)紅蘿蔔去皮切角形或切厚件。

(2)石九公洗淨滴乾水，用三湯匙油煎至兩面微黃色鏟起。（細條石九公不用劏，省去功夫，煲後隔去不要）

(3)水九杯或適量煲滾，加入石九公、紅棗、紅蘿蔔、薑煲滾後用中慢火煲一小時。

(4)取出石九公棄掉，取起紅棗、紅蘿蔔洗去魚骨，放回湯內再煲滾，下鹽調味盛湯碗內上桌。

註：

石九公是魚的名稱，也可用其他小魚煲此湯。魚滾豆腐蔬菜湯多喝了，不妨試試用紅棗紅蘿蔔煲，味道更鮮甜。

SMALL GROUPER WITH CARROT SOUP

Ingredients:
1 lb grouper (small)
1$\frac{1}{3}$ lb carrots
10 dried red dates (stones removed)
a slice ginger

Method:

1. Remove the skin of carrot and cut into triangular shapes.
2. Wash small grouper and drain. Fry with 3 tbsp oil until both sides are golden.
3. Boil 9 cups of water. Add fishes, dried red dates, carrots and ginger. Bring to boil. Simmer for an hour.
4. Dispose fishes. Take out the dried red dates and carrot to wash away the fish bones. Put into soup again. Bring to boil. Add salt and serve in bowl.

勝瓜滾魚片湯

用料：

勝瓜一個約重半斤(勝瓜又叫絲瓜)，鮮草菇三両，鯇魚肉三両(不可去皮)，薑二片，葱一條。

調味：

水四杯半，雞粉一茶匙，古月粉少許，鹽四分三茶匙，生抽半湯匙，油一湯匙。

做法：

(1)草菇批去泥腳洗淨，每隻切開邊。

(2)在鑊中放下薑一片、葱一條、水一杯半煮滾，下草菇煮約五分鐘，撈起用清水洗淨，盛筲箕內滴乾水(薑葱不要)。

(3)勝瓜刨去外皮洗淨切片。

(4)鯇魚肉連皮洗淨抹乾水，白鑊(即不下油)煎鯇魚皮，二秒鐘取起，切雙飛片，排在碟上。(白鑊煎魚皮，使魚皮收縮，易熟又辟腥。切雙飛，即是第一片不可切斷，第二片才切斷)

(5)把調味、草菇和薑一片，一齊煲滾，放下勝瓜煲熟，落魚片快手兜勻，立即熄火，湯盛湯碗內，湯料盛碟上，一同上桌。

註：

可以用肉片或牛肉代替魚片。

GRASS CARP FILLETS WITH ANGLED LUFFA SOUP

Ingredients:
1 angled luffa (about 10 oz)
4 oz straw mushrooms
4 oz grass carp fillets (with skin)
2 slices ginger
1 stalk spring onion

Seasoning:

4½ cups water
1 tsp chicken powder
pinch of pepper
¾ tsp salt
½ tbsp light soy
1 tbsp oil

Method:

1. Remove the muddy bottom of straw mushrooms. Halve.
2. Put a slice of ginger, 1 stalk spring onion and 1½ cup water in wok. Bring to boil. Add straw mushrooms and cook for 5 minutes. Take out and wash. Drain. (Dispose the spring onion)
3. Remove the skin of angled luffa, wash and slice.
4. Wash grass carp fillets and wipe dry. Fry the skin of grass carp for 2 seconds without oil. Slice and place on plate.
5. Boil the seasoning together with straw mushrooms and a slice ginger. Add angled luffa and bring to boil. Put in fish fillets and quickly stir. Turn off heat. Serve soup in bowl and ingredients in plate.

老樹
黃瓜煲水蟹湯

用料：
老樹黃瓜一隻，重約一斤，水蟹一斤，豬蹍四両。

做法：
(1) 老樹黃瓜洗淨連皮切開邊，去瓤後切厚而大件。

(2) 水蟹洗淨劏後斬件。（用肉蟹煲湯當然可以，只是太不經濟了，水蟹價錢很平，煲成的湯很鮮美）

(3) 豬蹍放落滾水中煮五分鐘，取起洗淨。

(4) 水八杯或適量煲滾，加入黃瓜、水蟹、豬蹍煲滾後，慢火煲二小時。湯料上碟，湯加鹽調味，盛湯碗內齊上桌。

CRAB WITH CUCUAMBER SOUP

Ingredients:
1 cucumber (about $1\frac{1}{3}$ lb) fully mature
$1\frac{1}{3}$ lb crabs
5 oz shin of pork

Method:

1. Wash cucumber and halve. Remove the seeds and section.
2. Wash and chop up the crabs.
3. Put pork in boiling water to cook for 5 minutes. Take out and wash.
4. Boil 8 cups of water. Add cucumber, crabs and pork. Bring to boil and simmer for 2 hours. Serve the ingredients in plate. Add salt to soup and serve in bowl.

黃魚羹

用料：

黃花魚十兩（可用雪藏黃花魚），冬菇五隻，中國火腿剁幼一湯匙，中國芹菜一株（去葉切碎，沒有芹菜的季節免用），葱二條切碎，薑切幼粒半湯匙，雞蛋一隻拂勻。

調味：

麻油、古月粉少許，鹽半茶匙，生抽半湯匙，上湯四杯（或用四杯水，混和二茶匙雞粉代替上湯）。

獻：

粟粉三湯匙半，水半杯。

做法：

(1)黃花魚洗淨抹乾水，加酒半湯匙搽勻蒸熟，約蒸十五分鐘。冷後拆肉，骨不要。

(2)冬菇浸軟去腳，揸乾水切粒。

(3)下油一湯匙，落調味、冬菇、薑粒、魚肉煮滾；埋獻，試味，下芹菜、葱兜勻煮滾，熄火，加入雞蛋攪勻，盛湯碗內。

註：

上湯可到超級市場買罐頭清雞湯。

MANDARIN FISH SOUP

Ingredients:

¾ lb Mandarin fish (Wong-fah-yu) (frozen ones can be used)
5 black mushrooms
1 tbsp Chinese ham (minced)
1 stalk Chinese celery (leaves removed, diced)
2 stalks spring onion (minced)
½ tbsp ginger (minced)
1 egg (whisked)

Seasoning:

pinch of sesame oil

pinch of pepper
½ tsp salt
½ tbsp light soy
4 cups superior stock (or 2 tsp chicken powder mixed with 4 cups water)

Sauce:
3½ tbsp cornflour
½ cup water

Method:
1. Wash Mandarin fish and wipe dry. Rub on ½ tbsp wine. Steam for about 15 minutes till it's fully cooked. When cool, remove the bones from the fish.
2. Soak mushroom, trim, squeeze out excess water and dice.
3. Put 1 tbsp oil in wok, add seasoning, mushrooms, ginger and fish. Bring to boil, add sauce and taste. Put in celery and spring onion, bring to boil again. Turn off heat and add egg, stir well. Serve in bowl.

一品海皇羹

用料：

蝦仁四両，帶子六両，瑤柱四粒，膏蟹一斤，白菌十粒，沙葛切薄而小片約半杯（或用西蘭花莖代替），粉絲一両半，蛋白二隻拂勻。

醃料：

麻油、古月粉少許，生粉半湯匙，油半湯匙。

調味：

上湯六杯半，生抽半湯匙，麻油、古月粉少許，鹽一又四分一茶匙。

獻：

粟粉四湯匙，水半杯。

做法：

(1) 瑤柱加入浸過面之水，浸二小時，加糖半茶匙、酒一茶匙、古月粉少許，蒸一小時，冷後撕成幼條。

(2) 膏蟹蒸熟，約需十五分鐘，冷後取出蟹肉及蟹膏。

(3) 粉絲用清水浸軟，切短度，滴乾水。

(4) 白菌抹乾水，切幼粒。

(5) 帶子（如大粒切爲二粒）、蝦仁加醃料撈勻，放落滾水中灼熟撈起，滴乾水。

(6) 把調味、瑤柱、沙葛、白菌、粉絲同煮滾，埋獻。加入帶子、蝦仁、蟹肉、蟹膏煮滾，試味，下蛋白兜勻，盛湯碗內。

SUPREME SEAFOOD SOUP

Ingredients:

5 oz shrimps (shells removed)
4 conpoys
1$\frac{1}{3}$ lb green crabs
10 white mushrooms
½ cup Sar-kuk (Root of pueraria) (thinly sliced)
2 oz mungbean vermicelli
2 egg whites (whisked)

Seasoning (1):

pinch of sesame oil
pinch of pepper
½ tbsp cornflour
½ tbsp oil

Seasoning (2):

6½ cups superior stock
½ tbsp light soy
pinch of sesame oil
pinch of pepper
1¼ tsp salt

Sauce:

4 tbsp cornflour
½ cup water

Method:

1. Soak conpoy in water for 2 hours. Make sure that there will be enough water to cover the conpoy. Mix with ½ tsp sugar, 1 tsp wine and a pinch of pepper. Steam for an hour. Tear into

thin stripes when cool.

2. Steam the green crabs for 15 mintues until it's completely cooked. Take out the meat and roe.

3. Soak mungbean vermicelli, section and drain.

4. Wipe dry white mushrooms, dice.

5. Add seasoning (1) to conpoys and shrimps. Blanch in boiling water and drain.

6. Boil seasoning (2), conpoys, Sarkuk, white mushrooms and vermicelli. Add sauce, put in scallops, shrimps, crab meat and crab roe. Bring to boil. Taste and add egg. Stir well and serve in bowl.

鴿、鵪鶉、田雞、蛇

花膠燉鴿湯

用料：

瘦老鴿二隻，發起花膠八両，豬蹍四両，中國火腿半両，薑一片，酒一湯匙，滾水六杯或適量。

出水料：

薑一片，葱一條，酒半湯匙，油半湯匙，水二杯。

做法：

(1)瘦鴿、豬蹍放落滾水中煮十分鐘，取起洗淨。

(2)瘦鴿、豬蹍、火腿、薑、酒同放燉盅內，加滾水六杯或適量，冚密蓋燉三小時。

(3)花膠切件。

(4)把出水料煮滾，放下花膠煮約二分鐘，取起滴乾水，薑、葱不要。

(5)待瘦鴿燉到三小時，將花膠放入再燉半小時至四十分鐘。加入適量之鹽調味，原盅上桌。

註：

(1)花膠不能燉得太久，燉久了花膠會溶，湯似膠水。薄身的花膠燉半小時，厚身的燉四十分鐘。

(2)發起花膠可到海味店或超級市場買。

(3)花膠有養顏滋陰的功效。

(4)可以用一隻雞代替老鴿。

PIGEON AND FISH MAW SOUP

Ingredients:
2 pigeons (skinny ones)
10 oz fish maw (soaked)
5 of shin of pork
½ oz Chinese ham
a slice ginger
1 tbsp wine
6 cups boiling water

Ingredients for stewing the fish maw:
1 slice ginger
1 stalk spring onion
½ tbsp wine
½ tbsp oil
2 cup water

Method:
1. Put pigeon and pork in boiling water to cook for 10 minutes. Take out and wash.
2. Put pigeon, pork, ham, ginger, wine as well as 6 cups of boiling water into a steaming pot. Stew for 3 hours.

3. Slice fish maw.
4. Boil ingredients for stewing fish maw. Add fish maw to cook for 2 minutes. Drain and dispose ginger and spring onion.

5. When pigeon has been stewed for 3 hours, add fish maw and stew for another ½ hour to 40 minutes. Season with salt and serve in pot.

老鴿瘦肉湯

用料：

老鴿一隻，豬踭四両，果皮六分
一個(浸軟洗淨)。

做法：

(1)老鴿劏後洗淨，放落滾水中煮
　 五分鐘，取起洗淨。

(2)豬踭放落滾水中，煮五分鐘取
　 起，洗淨。

(3)水七杯或適量，下果皮煲滾，
　 下老鴿、豬踭煲滾後，慢火煲
　 二小時半至三小時。老鴿、豬
　 踭盛碟上，可蘸生抽熟油吃，
　 湯加鹽調味，盛湯碗內齊上
　 桌。

註：

老鴿、瘦肉加入果皮煲湯，除了
味鮮美、老少咸宜外，對小孩子
生熱痱有食療作用。

PIGEON AND LEAN PORK SOUP

Ingredients:
1 pigeon (old)
5 oz shin of pork
$1/_6$ dried tangerine peel (soaked and cleaned)

Method:

1. Wash pigeon and put in boiling water to cook for 5 minutes. Take out and wash.
2. Put the pork in boiling water to cook for 5 minutes. Take out and wash.
3. Boil 7 cups of water together with tangerine peel. Add pigeon and pork. Bring to boil. Simmer for 2½ hour to 3 hours. Serve pigeon and pork in plate. Season with light soy and cooked oil. Add salt to soup and serve in bowl.

蓮子芡實鵪鶉湯

用料：

鵪鶉四隻，瘦肉四両，蓮子一両，芡實一両，蜜棗四粒，果皮八分一個(浸軟洗淨)。

做法：

(1)蓮子去心，用清水浸三十分鐘，隔去水。(浸後易煲腍)

(2)鵪鶉劏後洗淨，放落滾水中煮十分鐘，瘦肉也放落滾水中煮五分鐘，取起洗淨。

(3)水九杯或適量，放入果皮煲滾，下鵪鶉、瘦肉、蓮子、芡實，煲滾後，慢火煲二小時半。瘦肉、鵪鶉盛碟上，湯加適量的鹽、生抽半湯匙調味齊上桌。

註：

可以用二隻瘦鴿代替鵪鶉。

QUAIL WITH LOTUS SEED AND FOX NUT SOUP

Ingredients:

4 quails
5 oz lean pork
1 oz lotus seeds
1 oz fox nuts
4 preserved dates

¹⁄₈ dried tangerine peel (soaked and cleaned)

Method:

1. Core the lotus seeds. Soak in water for 30 minutes, and drain.
2. Wash quails and put in boiling water to cook for 10 minutes, then add lean pork, cook for another 5 minutes. Take out and wash.
3. Boil 9 cups of water together with tangerine peel. Add quails, lean pork, lotus seeds and fox nuts. Bring to boil and simmer for 2½ hours. Serve pork and quail in plate. Add salt and ½ tbsp light soy to soup. Serve in bowl.

髮菜田雞湯

用料：

田雞一斤，髮菜半兩，冬菇半兩，薑三片，葱二條，酒半湯匙。

醃料：

薑汁半湯匙，生粉一茶匙。

做法：

(1)冬菇浸軟去腳，揸乾水，加生粉四分一茶匙撈勻。

(2)髮菜用清水浸十分鐘，洗淨揸乾水。

(3)田雞劏後洗淨斬大件，加醃料醃十分鐘。

(4)薑二片、葱二條、酒半湯匙、水四杯煮滾，放下田雞煮四分鐘，撈起滴乾水。髮菜也放下薑葱水內煮五分鐘撈起，揸乾水，切短。

(5)水六杯煲滾，下薑一片、田雞、髮菜煲滾，慢火煲二十五分鐘，放下冬菇再煲十五分鐘，加入適量鹽、生抽半湯匙調味。

註：

此湯功能滑大腸、去熱、去內臟塵。從事建築、理髮、司機者多飲有食療作用。

FROG AND FAT-CHOI SOUP

Ingredients:
1 ⅓ lb frog
½ oz Fat-choi
½ oz black mushrooms
3 slices ginger
2 stalks spring onion
½ tbsp wine

Seasoning:
½ tbsp ginger sauce
1 tsp cornflour

Method:

1. Soak mushrooms and trim, squeeze out excess water. Mix with ¼ tsp cornflour.
2. Soak Fat-choi for 10 minutes, wash and squeeze out excess water.
3. Skin, gut and thoroughly wash the frog. Chop and marinate with seasoning for 10 minutes.
4. Boil 4 cups of water together with 2 slices ginger, 2 stalks spring onion and ½ tbsp wine. Add frog to cook for 4 minutes. Take out and drain. Then put in Fat-choi to cook for 5 minutes. Take out to squeeze out excess water. Cut into short sections.
5. Boil 6 cups of water, add a slice of ginger, frog and Fat-choi. Bring to the boil. Reduce to a low simmer for 25 minutes. Add mushrooms and simmer for another 15 minutes. Add salt and ½ tbsp light soy to taste.

南棗黑雞燉三蛇

用料：

三蛇一副（買時請蛇店劏好，說明煲蛇湯用），南棗六粒（去核），光黑肉雞一隻，薑一片，滾水六杯或適量，酒半湯匙，果皮六分一個（浸軟洗淨）。

做法：

(1)三蛇、黑肉雞放落滾水中煮十分鐘，取起洗一洗。

(2)把蛇繞成蛇餅放在燉盅內，放一竹墊在蛇上（待蛇燉脸，蛇骨不至附在雞上），雞放在竹墊上，薑、酒、滾水放入燉盅內，佃密蓋燉四至五小時。取起蛇不要，隔去湯內的蛇骨。

(3)蛇湯、黑雞、南棗放回燉盅內，加鹽調味，再燉片刻，原盅上桌。

註：

(1)過樹龍、飯鏟頭、金腳帶稱為三蛇，加入白花蛇、三索綫稱為五蛇。

(2)蛇湯祛風去濕又滋補，煲或燉湯時，可加入所需之藥材。

BLACK DATES, CHICKEN AND SNAKE SOUP

Ingredients:

1 three types of snakes*
6 dried black dates (stones removed)
1 black-skinned chicken
a slice ginger
6 cups boiling water
½ tbsp wine
$1/_6$ dried tangerine peel

Method:

1. Put snakes and chicken into boiling water to cook for 10 minutes. Take out and wash.
2. Circle the snake and put into a steaming pot with a bamboo mat on top. Then place chicken on top of bamboo mat. Add boiling water, ginger, wine into pot. Stew for 4—5 hours. Dispose the snake and it's bones.
3. Put the soup, chicken, and dates back into pot. Add salt and stew for a while. Serve in pot.

* Buy from snake shop, one cobra, one golden-banded copper head and one bamboo sivake skinned, cleaned and poisons removed by experts of the snake shop.

其他

木須湯

用料:

番茄三隻重約六两,金針、雲耳共七錢(約三分二两),雞蛋二隻拂匀。

調味:

上湯四杯(或水四杯,混和雞粉二茶匙),古月粉少許,鹽四分三茶匙,糖三分一茶匙。

做法:

⑴金針、雲耳用清水浸一小時,洗淨。金針切去硬的部分,雲耳撕成小塊,同放落滾水中煮五分鐘撈起,洗淨滴乾水,這樣可去金針的酸味、雲耳的異味。

⑵番茄去核洗淨切件。如要去皮,可把番茄浸於滾水中五分鐘,取起便可撕去皮。

⑶下油一湯匙爆番茄,落調味、金針、雲耳煮滾,再煮片刻,試味,熄火,落雞蛋攪匀,即可盛湯碗內。

TOMATO AND EGG SOUP

Ingredients:

3 tomatoes (about 8 oz)
1 of dried white fungus and dried lily flowers
2 eggs (whisped)

Seasoning:

4 cups superior stock (or 2 tsp chicken powder mixed with 4 cups water)

pinch of pepper
¾ tsp salt
⅓ tsp sugar

Method:

1. Soak dried white fungus and dried lily flowers in water for an hour. Remove the hardest part of lily flowers, tear white fungus into little pieces. Put both into boiling water to cook for 5 minutes. Take out, wash and drain.

2. Remove the seeds of tomato, wash and chop. If the skin is to be removed, soak tomato in boiling water for 5 minutes. Take out and tear off the skin.

3. Saute tomatoes with 1 tbsp oil. Add seasoning, white fungus and lily flowers. Bring to boil. Cook for a while and taste. Turn off heat. Add egg and stir well. Serve in bowl immediately.

榨菜
粉絲滾蝦米湯

用料：

蝦米一両，榨菜一両，粉絲一両，葱二條切碎，薑一片。

做法：

(1)粉絲用清水浸軟切短度。

(2)榨菜洗淨切薄片。怕吃辣的，榨菜切薄片後，用清水浸半小時，多洗數次，以去鹹味和辣味。

(3)蝦米用清水浸十分鐘，洗淨滴乾水。

(4)下油一湯匙，爆薑及蝦米，加水四杯煮滾，慢火再煮五分鐘，落榨菜、粉絲煮滾後落葱，下鹽調味。

SZECHWAN PRESERVED VEGETABLE, MUNGBEAN VERMICELLI AND DRIED SHRIMP SOUP

Ingredients:

1 oz dries shrimps

1 oz Szechwan preserved vegetables

1 oz mungbean vermicelli
2 stalks spring onion (shredded)
1 slice ginger

Method:

1. Soak vermicelli in water. Section,
2. Wash preserved vegetables and slice thinly. Soak in water for ½ hour and wash in serveral change of water for those who

can't stand hot and piquant taste.
3. Soak dried shrimps in water for 10 minutes. Wash and drain.
4. Saute ginger and dried shrimps with 1 tbsp oil. Add 4 cups of water. Bring to boil and then simmer for 5 minutes. Add preserved vegetables and vermicelli. When boiling, add spring onion and season with salt.

粟米豆腐羹

用料：

粟米茸半罐，嫩板豆腐一件(約三英吋丁方)，葱二條切碎，雞蛋二隻拂勻。

調味：

上湯四杯(或用四杯水，混和一湯匙雞粉代替上湯)，麻油、古月粉少許，鹽四分三茶匙，糖半茶匙。

獻：

粟粉三湯匙，水半杯。

做法：

(1)板豆腐洗淨切粒，要豆腐更嫩滑，將豆腐底及面切去不要。

(2)下油一湯匙，落調味及粟米茸煮滾，埋獻，下豆腐煮滾，下葱，熄火，落雞蛋攪勻即成。

CORN AND BEANCURD SOUP

Ingredients:

½ can mashed corn
1 beancurd (about 3'' square)
3 stalks spring onion (chopped)
2 eggs (whisked)

Seasoning:

4 cups superior stock (or 1 tsp chicken powder mixed with 4 cups

water)
pinch of sesame oil
pinch of pepper
¾ tsp salt
½ tsp sugar

Sauce:
3 tbsp cornflour
½ cup water

Method:
1. Wash and dice beancurd, better peel off the top and the bottom part.
2、 Put 1 tbsp oil in wok, add seasoning and corn. Bring to boil. Add sauce and beancurd. Bring to boil again. Put in spring onion and turn off heat. Add egg and stir well.

菠菜忌廉湯

用料：

菠菜六両(或用莧菜)，忌廉鷄湯一罐(超級市場有賣)。

做法：

(1)菠菜洗淨，放落滾水中灼軟撈起，用清水洗淨，揸乾水切碎。

(2)將忌廉鷄湯倒入煲內慢火煮熱，邊煮邊攪動，逐少加入水二杯半或適量(視各人喜歡湯的稀濃而定)，煮滾後成稀糊，下古月粉少許，落鹽調味。將菠菜放入湯內攪勻煮滾，盛湯碗內上桌。

CREAM OF SPINACH SOUP

Ingredients:
8 oz spinach
1 can chicken cream soup

Method:

1. Wash spinach blanch in boiling water. Take out and wash. Squeeze out excess water. Chop.
2. Put cream soup in pot and simmer. Keep stirring all the time, then gradually add 2½ cups of water until the mixture is thick. Add a pinch of pepper. Season with salt to taste. Add spinach and stir well. Bring to boil. Serve in bowl.

雪裏蕻蠶豆湯

用料：

浸透蠶豆四両（浸透蠶豆可到南
貨店或豆腐芽菜檔買），雪裏蕻
三両。

做法：

(1)雪裏蕻洗淨揸乾水切碎（無須
浸水，但要多洗幾次，以去鹹
味）。

(2)蠶豆剝外殼，洗淨，加入浸過
面半吋之清水，煲滾後，慢火
煲腍，約需十五至二十分鐘。

(3)水四杯或適量（包括煲蠶豆的
水），落蠶豆、雪裏蕻煲滾，
加油一湯匙、古月粉少許。加
鹽調味，盛湯碗內上枱。可加
少許葱碎或芫荽在湯內。

註：

(1)煲蠶豆不可用太多水，用少量
水煲易腍。蠶豆腍後，然後加
入所需湯水的分量。

(2)可用乾的蠶豆，用清水浸數
天，浸透後便可剝外殼。

SUIT-NEI-HOONG AND BROAD BEAN SOUP

Ingredients:

6 oz soaked dried broad beans
4 oz preserved vegetable (Suit-nei-hoong)

Method:

1. Wash preserved vegetable in

several changes of water. Squeeze out excess water and shred.

2. Remove the membrane of beans and wash. Pour enough water into a pot to cover the beans. Bring to boil. Simmer for 15 to 20 minutes until it's tender.

3. Boil 4 cups of water, add beans and preserved vegetable. Bring to boil. Add 1 tbsp oil and a pinch of pepper. Season with salt. Serve in bowl, sprinkle with parsley or chopped spring onion.

鹹蛋節瓜湯

用料：

節瓜一隻約半斤（或用芥菜六兩），鹹蛋二隻。

做法：

(1)節瓜刮皮洗淨切片。

(2)水四杯或適量煮滾，下節瓜及鹹蛋黃，煮至節瓜腍、鹹蛋黃熟，加油一湯匙，下鹹蛋白攪勻煮熟（蛋白不用拂），下鹽調味，盛湯碗內上枱。

HAIRY GOURD AND SALTED EGG SOUP

Ingredients:
1 hairy gourd (about 10 oz)
2 salted eggs

Method:
1. Skin, wash and slice hairy gourd.
2. Boil 4 cups of water, add hairy gourd and egg yolks. Cook until hairy gourd is tender and egg yolks fully cooked. Add 1 tbsp oil, put in egg whites. Keep stirring until it's fully cooked. Taste, add salt if necessary, serve soup in bowl.

墨魚煲木瓜湯

用料：

新鮮墨魚一隻，重約十二両，排骨半斤(斬件)，銀耳半両，半生熟木瓜一隻，重約十二両(可到菜檔買)，薑一片。

做法：

(1)木瓜去皮去核洗淨，切厚件。

(2)銀耳用清水浸約二小時，洗淨撕成小朵，放落滾水中煮五分鐘，取起用清水洗淨，滴乾水。

(3)墨魚劏好，撕去外衣洗淨。

(4)墨魚、排骨放落滾水中煮五分鐘，取起洗淨。

(5)水九杯或適量煲滾，放下墨魚、排骨、木瓜、銀耳、薑煲滾後，慢火煲二小時。湯料切件盛碟上。湯加鹽調味，盛湯碗內，一齊上桌。

CUTTLFISH AND PAPAYA SOUP

Ingredients:
1 cuttlefish (about 1 lb)
10 oz spare ribs (chopped)
½ oz dried white fungus
1 papaya (about 1 lb)
a slice ginger

Method:
1. Skin papaya and remove the

seeds, section.

2. Soak white fungus for 2 hour. Wash and tear into little pieces. Put in boiling water to cook for 5 minutes. Take out and wash. Drain.

3. Remove the membrane of cuttlefish. Wash.

4. Put cuttlefish and spare ribs in boiling water to cook for 5 minutes. Take out and wash.

5. Boil 9 cups of water, put in cuttlefish, spare ribs, white fungus and ginger. Bring to boil and immediately reduce to a low simmer for 2 hours. Serve the ingredients in plate. Add salt to soup to taste and serve in bowl.

本书原名为《汤羹》，原出版者为香港博益出版集团有限公司，经授权由广东科技出版社在中国大陆地区出版发行。

图书在版编目（CIP）数据

广东风味菜　汤羹/李曾鹏展著

—广州：广东科技出版社，1996.6

ISBN　7-5359-1669-4

Ⅰ．广⋯

Ⅱ．李⋯

Ⅲ．菜谱-广东

Ⅳ.TS972

出版发行：广东科技出版社
　　　　　（广州市环市东路水荫路 11 号　邮编：510075）
经　　销：广东省新华书店
印　　刷：广东惠阳印刷厂
规　　格：889×1194　1/16　4 印张　字数 80 千
版　　次：1996 年 6 月第 1 版
　　　　　1996 年 6 月第 1 次印刷
印　　数：0001—5000 册
ＩＳＢＮ 7-5359-1669-4
分 类 号：TS·99
定　　价：20.00 元

广东省版权局著作权合同登记
图字 19-1996-011 号